BERNARD NOBEL

(516) OR-1-3911

WALKER SUN BOOKS

The Origins of Life

A SUN BOOK

The Origins of Life

JULES CARLES

Doctor of Sciences; Doctor of Letters

Translated from the French by Francis Huxley

A SUN BOOK

 Walker and Company · New York

Preface

The problem of origins is always disturbing. Once there was a time, which we cannot remember, when we did not exist. . . .

However, nearly everything that now surrounds us existed when, at a certain date, which we know, we began our cautious adventure and—for a limited time—took our place in the sun.

Before us, there was life. We are descended from living cells produced by organisms that have preceded us on the earth, and our ancestors also were given life by yet more ancient beings of the same kind and of the same race. Throughout our past our line of descent is continuous, for if we can disappear without leaving descendants, we cannot appear if we do not have two parents; and so we trace our line, without the least break in continuity, until we reach the first man. Evolution invites us to go back even further, to living creatures progressively simpler, as far as the first living thing, which had no parents to give it life.

The problem of the origin of life thus appears to us in different forms, and at different stages. Those who believe in ·evolution say that there is only one origin to be explained, that of the very first living being; while our ancestors in the Middle Ages, who had no idea of evolution, could not think beyond the first individual of each species and therefore had to solve the problem of origins for each one of them. Between these two positions all kinds of variations existed, and spontaneous reproduction was something so unremarkable that for a long time it was thought that a certain number of species could either reproduce themselves normally or arise spontaneously, without needing parents.

Be that as it may, the problem of origins that we are taking up is not at all that of ordinary reproduction: this is only an origin from the individual's point of view, and not from the point of view of the species, which uses reproduction to maintain itself. Reproduction refers to the birth of a creature from one or two parents who, by means of a part of their bodies, transmit life to that creature, at the same time as its heredity. We shall consider the various ways in which life originated not covered by this definition, either because the new being was fabricated rather than engendered by the animal or plant that gave it life, or because it sprang from that which was not alive.

This kind of birth is called by many different names. In the Middle Ages it was called *equivocal generation,* or pseudo-generation. The best-known name is *spontaneous generation,* but this really means very little, because in order to be spontaneous one must already exist. Nothing like this can happen with spontaneous generation, because by definition that which was so engendered did not exist at the moment when it spontaneously decided to be born. Then would this spontaneity be that of another living creature? Evidently not, because then we would have to speak of making or creating. Can we appeal to the spontaneity of matter? Surely these words cannot be used together.

Another term is *abiogenesis*. This refers to the appearance of a living creature from non-living matter. But this expression is as incomprehensible as the preceding one. *Biogenesis* means origin or formation of life, just as *embryogenesis* means origin or formation of the embryo. When it is preceded by the negative *a-*, the sense of the word must be translated as "absence of the formation of life," or "absence of biogenesis" (just as chromatopsia means "color vision" and achromatopsia "absense of color vision"); this is exactly the opposite of what is meant.

For the sake of clarity we will not use the terms "equivocal generation" and "spontaneous generation," and certainly not "abiogenesis." We think the simplest is also the best word to use; when talking of generation where life is not transmitted, we will use the term "biogenesis," which in one word lucidly expresses the phrase "origin of life." It will be convenient to use this term whenever the actual transmission of life is not in question, whether we are talking of the very first living thing or of that made by the scientist in his laboratory.

Biogenesis is a vast problem, for it has always fascinated man; and to treat it in full would take many volumes. We shall try to describe it, adequately if not completely, by taking up the various positions from which it can be attacked.

The first chapter will give a general account of the history of the problem, with special reference to Pasteur, whose name dominates the subject.

The second will try to define the gap that separates matter from life, and to remind us of the precautions we must take if we are to avoid making stupid blunders.

The third will describe the research that has gone toward finding intermediate forms that might bridge this mysterious gap.

When we have looked at the problem from all angles and established the main facts, we will examine the answers given by philosophy, science and history. Philosophy tries to make us understand what biogeny is (Chapter 4); science constructs hypotheses to show us how things might have happened (Chapter 5); and paleontology (Chapter 6) endeavors, insofar as it can, to demonstrate just how in fact things came to pass.

JULES CARLES

Contents

Contents

The Origins of Life

A SUN BOOK

1 / The History of Biogeny

Ever since agriculture began on our planet, men have found that domesticated animals and useful plants require constant care if they are to multiply, while wild animals swarm in great numbers, as do the weeds in the fields, which men are sure they did not sow. In contrast to sheep, dogs and wheat, which are sometimes only bred with difficulty, poppies, flies, snakes and rats multiply spontaneously.

Antiquity and the Renaissance

Biogenesis thus did not appear such an extraordinary fact, and it holds a fairly important place in ancient literature. In his *Metamorphoses*, Ovid tells us that Deucalion and Pyrrha repeopled the earth after the devastation of the flood by sowing stones that became men, while various animals sprang up from the earth.

In a passage that we shall quote below, Lucretius also describes the earth as engendering all living things, chance taking a hand in the creation of numerous mon-

strosities that fail to survive, though there are also success-
ful forms that live and reproduce.

Virgil has a long description in the *Georgics* of how
bees originate in the entrails of a bull that has been killed
in a particular way and left to rot. This expensive method
can hardly have been tried very often by beekeepers, or
their faith in Virgil's authority would soon have been
shaken.

It would be easy to select quaint texts on biogeny from
the Middle Ages, but let us concentrate on the naturalists.

Aristotle (384–322 B.C.), the first true biologist, was
a precise and careful observer and discovered numerous
forms of reproduction unknown until then, certain of which
presuppose prodigious observation. Working so many centuries before the invention of the microscope, and the later
discovery of the nature of fertilization, he cannot be re-
proached for having missed the microscopic eggs of molluscs, worms and so forth. Biogenesis lost much ground
with him, but even so he was left with an immense field,
and until the seventeenth century no one disputed his
authority in it.

Neither Rome nor the Middle Ages had any interest in scientific research, and we cannot reproach the
men of those times for believing facts that even the most
distinguished scholars of the Renaissance considered true.

Ambroise Paré (1517–1590), the most famous surgeon
of his century, tells us one such fact in a personal story:
"Being in one of my vineyards near the village of Meudon,
where I was having large and solid rocks broken up, a
live toad was found in one of them, though there was no

apparent opening: and I marveled at this animal having been born, grown and stayed alive there. But the stone-breaker told me there was no reason to marvel, for he had many times found such toads or other animals in depths of a stone without an opening. One can also give the reason for the birth and growth of such animals: it is that they are engendered in some damp substance coming from stone, and this dampness, when putrefying, produces such animals."

At the beginning of the seventeenth century, Van Helmont (1577–1644), the greatest physiologist of the time, noted down a whole series of curious recipes for biogenesis; the most famous is the one in which he proposes to create mice. A jar is filled with wheat and its mouth stopped with a dirty shirt—a woman's shirt, if possible. "A leaven coming from the shirt, transformed by the smell of the seeds, changes the corn itself into mice." This metamorphosis takes about twenty-one days, which is just the time of gestation in the mouse, and Van Helmont was astonished at this extraordinary speed. "What is even more remarkable," he says, "is that the mice which come from the corn and the shirt are not small, are not still at the teat, neither dwarf nor premature, but are very well formed and can jump."

At this time Father Athanasius Kircher (1602–1680), the famous professor of science in the College of Rome, had not the slightest doubt about these metamorphoses, and in his *Mundus subterraneus* he makes several personal observations:

Among small Laburnum twigs, which is called white vine, I have often found a zoophyte (animal-plant) with the bearing of a spider, whose very thin body has six legs and a head like a caterpillar; in searching carefully for the place where this insect comes, I succeeded in discovering that it was born from the small fertilized twigs of this Laburnum, which are invaded by putrefaction; and many a time I have been able to find this creature born on a yet green twig, and with good reason I have called it xylophyte; for I have found many whose hind parts were still of wood, while the front part had life, which made them move here and there. I have seen some the middle of whose body, supported by legs, was identical with the wood of a small Laburnum twig, while the heads and legs were already stirring with life: as soon as the pith of the small twig with its six little branches is transformed into a living creature, the animal separates itself from the trunk and moves like other six-legged insects. When I showed this stupefying metamorphosis to many of my colleagues, it is impossible to say how much they admired such a rare and even monstrous birth, above all when they saw the front part of the body moved by its legs, while the hind part was still attached to the trunk.

One of this author's most celebrated works is his abundantly illustrated *Arca Noe,* which gives a long description of the famous Ark, built to save man and the animals from the flood. The animals can be divided into two large groups: those that reproduce by normal methods, and those that are born by spontaneous generation. It is obviously pointless to give these latter a place in the already encumbered Ark. One passage from this book shows us that this Jesuit scholar was well informed about the science of his day, for he talks of an "extravagant personage," a certain *Francesco Redi* (1626–1691), who dared to utter doubts about biogenesis: "This scholarly and most perspicacious doctor of the Grand Duke of Etruria has published a small book on the generation of insects in which he denies that putrefaction can give birth to these animals. Further, pushed by I know not what spirit of contradiction, he attacks my experiments. . . ."

Redi, however, was right: there are maggots in meat, not because it produces them, but because flies have been allowed to settle there. In a well-stoppered flask, maggots do not appear on meat, and even if one merely wraps the meat in gauze, one can see the flies trying to come as close as possible, and often laying their eggs on the gauze; these eggs can give rise to maggots and flies, if they are then placed on some meat.

These remarkably simple experiments opened the way to future discoveries and—unexpected result—made a step forward in our material culture: Redi had just invented the pantry.

The famous axiom *Omne vivum e vivo*, announced by Vallisnieri, Redi's disciple, was nonetheless much less clear than it seems nowadays. "Every living thing comes from another living thing," certainly; but if, for example, the intestines or perhaps the corpse of an animal produces small worms, can we say that the principle has been violated? It does, however, remain true that the problem of the appearance of life made a great step forward, and that Redi foreshadowed future discoveries when he wrote: "I felt myself disposed to believe that the earth, since the first plants and the first animals that it produced in the first days of the world at the command of the sovereign and omnipotent Creator, has never again produced by herself plants, trees or any kind of animal whether perfect or imperfect, and that everything which in the past has been born and which now is born in her or from her, comes from the true and real seed of those same plants and of animals that maintain their kind by means of their proper seed."

The end of the seventeenth century saw the appearance of the microscope, and naturalists turned their attention toward the small animalcules, which they were surprised to find so marvelously organized, so complex in their smallness. How could such creatures be anything but the outgrowths or products of the decomposition of some piece of meat? But we see a new way of thinking among the scholars, who find themselves less and less at ease with all these old theories of biogenesis. With prophetic assurance Fontenelle writes in his little book, *On the Existence of God:* "Every animal that seems to come either from putrefaction or from warmed and moistened dust comes in reality from seed that we have not noticed. . . . All modern experiments conspire to disabuse us of this ancient error, and I am quite sure that in a short time there will not remain the least cause for doubt."

The First Controversy

Progress was slower in coming than Fontenelle had supposed. Indeed, the year 1745 marks the date of a vigor-

ous counteroffensive. An Irishman, Needham (1713–1781),
carried out some surprising experiments with water and
pieces of meat inside flasks. Closing the flasks carefully with
cork stoppers, he surrounded them with cinders hot enough
to cook an egg and therefore to kill all life: which did not
stop this meat from teeming with animalcules, just like
meat that had not been exposed to such heat. It was thus
obvious that these animalcules were produced by the
meat during its putrefaction: "The heat killed all the germs
that existed in the infusion at the beginning, germs that
came from the sides of the flask, from the water, from the
matter being infused or from the air; the flask being hermetically sealed, no living thing could creep in after the
heating. It is thus evident that the germs which we find
there are born by spontaneous generation."

Buffon, who treated the lower animals with scorn, did
not hesitate to take sides with Needham and talked of
organic molecules liberated by putrefaction and coming
together to form the simpler organisms. Whereas Bonnet,
and above all Réaumur, who had specialized in the study
of these allegedly simpler creatures, rebelled against these
explanations and against Needham's experiments; and Vol-
taire went so far as to call Needham an impostor and a
Jesuit.

At this moment a celebrated Italian experimenter
came on the scene: Spallanzani (1729–1799). His first experiments confirmed Needham's results, but he later per-
fected his experimental conditions: thus in place of the
cork stoppers he sealed his flasks by melting the glass, and

he prolonged the heating for an hour in boiling water. No life at all appeared in the flasks so treated, and Spallanzani immediately proclaimed against biogenesis.

Needham replied that these experiments were not conclusive because they were distorted by too much heating: "Spallanzani hermetically sealed nineteen flasks, filled with a variety of vegetable matter, and boiled them when so closed for an hour. But from the way he treated and tortured these nineteen vegetable infusions it is obvious that not only had he very much weakened or even totally destroyed the vegetative force of the substances being infused, but also that he had entirely corrupted, by exhalations and the strength of the heat, the little quantity of air that remained in the empty part of the flasks. It is not surprising, therefore, that the infusions so treated gave no sign of life. It should be that way."

Spallanzani set himself to reply to these two objections, that the vegetative force had been destroyed and the air vitiated. That the vegetative force persisted, on the contrary, was seen from the fact that germs developed on the boiled substances when they were put in the open air; however, it was much harder to prove that the air inside had not become vitiated, because oxygen had not yet been discovered and no one knew just what air was.

This scientific discussion between opposite ends of Europe shows that science was already international. Once again, domestic economy was to profit from these theoretical controversies: The Parisian confectioner Appert, realizing that putrefaction does not occur in flasks that have been hermetically sealed and then boiled, put into practice a method for making preserves, and in 1811 published an enthusiastic book on his system: "The author does not pretend to be the first who has conserved peas in glass, but his method is practical and sure. What then is this principle of conservation that works such marvels? It is heat, it is fire. This principle, so wholly pure, works in the same way and has the same effects on every kind of foodstuff; it is its beneficent action that, in releasing them from fermentation, which is always destructive, or in neutralizing it, impresses them with this seal of incorruptibility, that produces such happy results."

The preserves were excellent, even if the explanation was not, and their fame was a reminder of the insoluble problem. Gay-Lussac had analyzed the air present in these preserves, and found it lacking in oxygen. Was Needham right, then, in saying that heat vitiated the air and that biogenesis was impossible in an atmosphere that could not support life?

The Work of Pasteur

During the first half of the nineteenth century no advance was made in the problem, and no one dared to venture into this dangerous field. However, Pouchet (1800–1876), director of the Museum of Natural History at Rouen, took up the cudgels for biogenesis in a note to the Academy of Sciences on December 20, 1858, and followed it up the next year with a large work, *Heterogeneity, or a Treatise on Spontaneous Generation:* "When I realized through meditation that spontaneous generation was still one of the ways nature used to produce living creatures, I set about to discover by what means one could bring these phenomena to light."

Such a categorical affirmation aroused many protests, and Pasteur, who was already interested in these problems, wrote to Pouchet: "I think you are wrong, not in believing in spontaneous generation (for it is difficult in such a case not to have a preconceived idea), but in affirming it. In the experimental sciences it is always wrong to be sure when the facts do not force one to an affirmation. . . . In my opinion the question is still completely open and undecided."

But Pouchet considered he could prove his point. Holding a flask full of boiled and distilled water upside down in a basin of mercury, he unstoppered it, introduced a little oxygen and nitrogen made by chemical means, and then slipped in a wad of hay from another flask that had been sterilized for twenty minutes. After several days, the water was crowded with microorganisms.

Pasteur suspected that a little "common air" had been introduced, and that microbes had been present on the surface of the mercury. After having considered the matter for a long time, he embarked on those famous experiments that were to settle the problem for good and bring the age-long debate to a close.

Pasteur thought that the air was full of microbes, which only needed a favorable environment to develop. In his small laboratory at the Ecole Normale he let in air from the rue d'Ulm through a wad of cotton, which became covered, not only with dust, but with microbes, as he found when he inoculated a culture medium with the polluted cotton.

The air is thus filled with microbial germs, but they

become rarer the further one is from towns. Taking some glass flasks, Pasteur introduced some culture media, boiled them and sealed the narrow necks with a welding lamp. No putrefaction appeared in such flasks.

He took twenty flasks and went into a Paris street. He broke the narrow necks: a little air entered the flasks, which had been sealed when hot. He sealed them once more, and soon all twenty flasks were seen to be contaminated.

The same experiment carried out at Arbois showed that the air there was much purer, since only eight of the flasks were contaminated. On top of the small mountain of Pou-pet (850 meters high) only five were contaminated, and on the Mer de Glace, at 2,000 meters, only one in twenty was. The precautions taken were remarkably precise, as Vallery-Radot tells us: "After having made a scratch on the glass with a steel blade, he began to heat the thin neck of each flask in the flame of a small alcohol lamp, in order to destroy the dust, which would have been a cause of error. Then, holding the flask above his head directly away from the wind, he broke the tip with an iron pincers, whose long arms had also been passed through the flame in order to burn the dust that could have stuck to their surface and that might have been sucked into the flask by the sudden entry of air. Out of these twenty flasks, resealed on the spot, only one was contaminated."

Pasteur was able to end his experiments by saying: "It seems to me that we can affirm that the exclusive origin, the first and necessary condition of life in these infusions, is the dust in suspension in the air."

He proved this in another way. The flask is not contaminated if one kills the microbes in the air that is allowed to enter. To do this, the air is made to go through a red-hot tube of platinum; all the microbes in the air are killed during the passage, and the flask is not contaminated after being resealed.

But, we may object, this air is vitiated, burned out by the heat and incapable of maintaining life. Yet this does not hold. There are other ways of purifying air, for example, by passing it through water, which will absorb all the microbes if the air passes slowly enough. Pasteur made flasks whose necks were very long and curved into an S-shape. Filling one of the curves of the S was a little water, through which the air had to pass. The result was the same as for the previous experiment: none of the flasks were contaminated.

There remained Needham's former objection, that prolonged boiling killed the vegetative force. Can an organism remain unputrefied even without the use of heat? Convinced that all germs came from the air, Pasteur took careful samples of the body's liquids—blood, urine and so forth—and put them into hermetically sealed flasks. No putrefaction took place, because the living body normally does not contain microbes, and those in the air had been excluded from the flasks.

From these experiments sprang one of the greatest therapeutic discoveries of modern times, asepsis. Every surgeon and nurse now knows that his first duty is to keep wounds free from the microbes in the air, because, as Lecomte du Noüy has pointed out, the wound heals itself at its own rhythm once surgery is completed, and our only duty is to stop germs from interfering in this progress toward recovery. The idea of asepsis, propagated by Lister in England, became a fundamental rule in medicine: it meant that all the instruments used in surgery had to be rigorously sterilized, together with everything that came into contact with the wound. Discussion on the origin of life thus continued to produce important, fruitful and practical results.

Pouchet, however, did not consider himself defeated, and continued experimenting. Pasteur had opened his flasks in the Alps at an altitude of 2,000 meters; Pouchet, accompanied by Joly and Musset, opened his on the Maladetta mountain chair in the Pyrenees, at an altitude of 3,000 meters. All the flasks became filled with living organisms, and Pouchet defied Pasteur by affirming that such must always be the case, as soon as a little oxygen enters the flasks.

An academic commission was nominated on January 4, 1864, to carry out a series of well-planned experiments in the Museum of Natural History. The heterogenists, who had their own program, protested and withdrew, leaving Pasteur to carry out the experiments alone. The irony of the incident lies in the fact that, had they stayed and carried out their experiments, they would probably have emerged triumphant; for Pouchet, instead of using yeast-water like Pasteur, was using hay infusion. Now hay infusion contains germs that are not killed at 100° C., and that develop immediately on receiving oxygen. Pasteur discovered this later, and observed that he could not be sure of killing every germ unless he raised the temperature to 120° C.: the sterilizer was thus to become the classic instrument for asepsis.

But Pouchet lacked persistence, and his debate with Pasteur hardly advanced the solution of the problem. It was a different matter with a London professor, Dr. Bastian, who forced Pasteur to follow such precise techniques in his experiments that no doubt could enter in.

Of the experiments that, according to Bastian, proved biogenesis, the simplest was as follows. Urine was boiled and left in a sealed flask, where it remained sterile and limpid for an indefinite time. When a few drops of potash were added, the urine became cloudy and full of bacteria: the potash thus stimulated biogenesis.

Being still ignorant of the fact that certain bacteria do not die at a temperature of 100°, Pasteur thought that the germs were carried in the potash, and challenged Bastian to carry out his experiment by calcining the potash before adding it. Bastian came to Paris in 1877 to take up the challenge, but after several days of lively discussion he returned to England, refusing to submit to the Commission's conditions. It is possible that he, like Pouchet, also missed enjoying an ephemeral triumph.

Pasteur, searching not for success but for truth, did not have to suffer defeat in order to continue pursuing his investigations: he saw the necessity not only for the sterilizer, but for passing all instruments and apparatus through a naked flame. Germs scattered in the air or in water can come to rest on instruments or inside flasks during washing, and can endure temperatures above 120°, especially if they are dry. To be destroyed they must be exposed to a flame, which deals with them the more effectively the drier they are. In Bastian's experiments the urine contained germs that had not been killed by heat and that could not develop because of the acidity of the medium; they began to reproduce when the medium became alkaline.

In this way, little by little, everything was explained, the exceptions were dealt with and Pasteur could repeat what he had already stated in 1864: "Spontaneous generation among microscopic creatures is a chimera. No, there is no known circumstance today in which one can say that microscopic creatures have arisen in the world except from seed, from parents similar to them. Those who believe otherwise have been the playthings of illusion, of badly carried out experiments, blotted by errors that they either could not see or did not know how to avoid."

And then, just as the victory appeared complete, there came the last and by no means the least attack. The papers of Claude Bernard, who had just died, were published in the *Revue Scientifique* of July, 1878. There Bernard said that the important thing in fermentation was not the microbes but the ferments, so that it was possible that the microbes came from the ferments.

We must understand that the process of fermentation was not understood at this time. Bacteria nourish themselves by secreting digestive juices that attack, break down and digest everything which will serve as food; various toxins, penicillin and streptomycin are such juices. The higher organisms contain in their own tissues active substances, called *diastases*, which can be set free just by crushing. Pasteur thought that fermentation was the direct consequence of the action of living things, while Bernard guessed at the existence of soluble ferments, and exaggerated their importance to the point of making them responsible not only for fermentation but for the appearance of the microbes themselves.

For Bernard, therefore, fermentation began without germs, and as it proceeded produced those germs that Pasteur affirmed were indispensable for the occurrence of fermentation. Today we know that, contrary to what Pasteur thought, fermentation is caused by the direct action of ferments, and that germs have no part in it except to produce these ferments; but we also know that the ferments are incapable of changing into germs or of causing their appearance.

Thus the debate began on a shaky footing. Pasteur did not deny that germs became numerous toward the end of fermentation, but he affirmed that fermentation began with germs already present. He insisted on the point that was not essential, but all the same managed to conclude that if microorganisms had not been introduced into the medium, they would not have appeared.

Without losing a day, Pasteur had a hermetically sealed greenhouse constructed and took it to Arbois, where he placed it over some of his vines, the grapes of which were then ripening. At that time there were no microbes to be found on them, although they settle on the grapes as they grow larger: it is their presence that causes fermentation when the grapes are crushed after the harvest. To be even more certain of keeping the germs off his grapes, Pasteur

wrapped them in cotton. In October the grapes were har-
vested with all necessary precautions, were crushed and
were placed in the mild temperature of a hothouse, in
which fermentation should have been encouraged: but no
fermentation took place, though in the same circumstances
other grapes of the same vine began to ferment in forty-
eight hours. For fermentation to take place in his protected
grapes it was only necessary to expose them to the fresh air
for a certain time, or to add a few of the unprotected
grapes. This demonstration was conclusive: only one element had been missing, the germs nothing else could replace or create.

So ended the long debate that had stirred the scientific
world for so many years. As the years strip away the ir-
relevancies, Pasteur appears a giantlike figure, who con-
tradicted and reversed a whole current of thought. In 1876
he wrote, on first hearing about Bastian's experiments:

> More fortunate than the inventors of perpetual mo-
> tion, the heterogenists have been able to rouse interest
> among scientific bodies for a long time. Mathematicians dis-
> dain reading any paper that deals with squaring the circle
> or perpetual motion; however, the subject of so-called
> spontaneous generation has always had the privilege of
> arousing public interest, because it is impossible in the
> present stage of science to prove, a priori, that life cannot
> appear at a bound independent of all similar and anterior
> life. Whenever anyone announces that he has found a
> way of bringing about spontaneous generation, he can be
> assured of support from all his fellow doctrinaires and of
> awakening doubts in those who have but a more or less

superficial knowledge of the subject. Here I have been searching for nearly twenty years to find life arising from no anterior life, without success. The consequences of such a theory would be incalculable. The natural sciences in general, medicine and philosophy, would receive a shock whose consequences no one can see. Also, whenever I learn that I have been outdone, I run after the fortunate investigator, ready to check his assertions. It is true that I run after him full of defiance. So many times I have found that, in this difficult art of experimentation, even the most skillful trip at each step and that the interpretation of the facts is not less dangerous!

Now, thanks to him, the position is reversed and biologists have become almost as inattentive to pronouncements about the discovery of biogenesis as physicists are to those of perpetual motion. It is no longer the adversaries of biogenesis but its partisans who must prove their assertions.

What a long road it has been from the beliefs of antiquity! The idea that living things could be born out of non-living matter was so firmly rooted in men's minds that it retreated only slowly, step by step, having to be dislodged progressively from all its positions. The meticulous observations of naturalists continually decreased the size of the animals that were thought to be produced in this fashion. Ambroise Paré's toads and the mice of Van Helmont were long gone when Redi came to deny the biogenesis of flies! The microscope opened up the world of microbes and helped to prove that here, too, biogenesis was absent. A doctrine finds it hard to survive the disappearance of its last foundations.

"Science," Pasteur could conclude, "must not worry itself about the philosophical consequences of its researches. If, by the development of my experimental studies, I was able to demonstrate that matter could organize itself into a cell or a living creature, I would proclaim it within these walls with the legitimate pride of an inventor who knows he has made a crucial discovery, and I would add, were I provoked: so much the worse for those whose doctrines or systems do not correspond with the truth of observable fact! It is with the same pride that I told you a moment ago, defying my adversaries to contradict me: in the present state of knowledge, the doctrine of spontaneous generation is a chimera. And I add with the same independence: so much the worse for those whose philosophical or political ideas are embarrassed by my studies!"

This is the way that science progresses. Often encumbered by preconceived ideas, it always ends by having the last word: for, throughout its researches and its vicissitudes, it is guided by its passionate desire for the truth.

2 / The Gap To Be Bridged

This history of biogenesis presupposes certain facts that must be admitted if the question is to have any meaning. The most fundamental is that life is radically distinct from matter, and this distinction is hardly contested.[1] Before proceeding, we must examine these facts and the essential points by which life is distinguished from inert matter, in constitution, structure and behavior.

Life's Chemical Constitution

If the living differs from the non-living, this is not primarily because of its chemical constitution or because of the substances of which, in the last analysis, it is composed. Living things contain no chemical element not found in the environment, and this is hardly strange since living

[1] However, let us note, by way of curiosity, the opinion of D. H. Salman: a return to the opinions of the Middle Ages, which never suspected the importance of the gap separating matter from the lower organisms, a gap defined by Pasteur's genius. According to Salman, therefore, the problem we are considering is one of those pseudo-problems that a philosopher has the right to ignore!

things use the elements within their reach. All the same, we can note certain differences in the concentration of elements: living things concentrate carbon and nitrogen (the basis of organic compounds) and sometimes certain metals, such as iodine in seaweed, or phosphorus in bone.

If we consider the ensemble of what Suess calls the *biosphere*—the mass of everything with which life is in contact, the atmosphere, hydrosphere and lithosphere—and compare the list of the elements that enter into its composition with those that make up a human body or a plant like alfalfa, we will notice striking similarities, and we will have to go into detail to uncover the differences. On both lists oxygen is the most important element; then, in the biosphere, comes silicon, owing to the quantity of silica and silicates in the mineral kingdom, while living matter uses carbon compounds.

Above all, life uses the light atoms and the metalloids. If we consider the first ten elements in the three lists, we find only three in the biosphere, compared with seven in animals and plants. The total proportion of metalloids among all the elements of the biosphere is only 79 per cent, while it reaches 98 per cent in man and 99 per cent in plants.

We can also note that life is more selective than the biosphere and has a marked prediliction for certain elements, to such a degree that in alfalfa five elements, and in man seven, form 99 per cent of the total composition, compared with the biosphere, whose first twelve elements hardly make up this percentage.

Besides these differences between inorganic and living

matter, those between animals and plants are minimal: animals are characterized by the abundance of nitrogen because of their proteins, by the calcium of their bones, and by the predominance of sodium over potassium, while plants have much more potassium than sodium.

THE COMPONENTS OF BIOSPHERE, ANIMALS AND PLANTS

Biosphere		*Animal*		*Plant*	
Elements					
Oxygen	50.02	Oxygen	62.81	Oxygen	77.90
Silica	25.80	Carbon	19.37	Carbon	11.34
Aluminum	7.30	Hydrogen	9.31	Hydrogen	8.72
Iron	4.18	Nitrogen	5.14	Nitrogen	0.825
Calcium	3.22	Calcium	1.38	Phosphorus	0.706
Sodium	2.36	Sulphur	0.64	Calcium	0.58
Potassium	2.28	Phosphorus	0.63	Potassium	0.2265
Magnesium	2.08	Sodium	0.26	Sulphur	0.1037
Hydrogen	0.95	Potassium	0.22	Magnesium	0.082
Titanium	0.43	Chlorine	0.18	Chlorine	0.07
Chlorine	0.20	Magnesium	0.04	Sodium	0.0393
Carbon	0.18	Iron	0.005	Silica	0.0093
Phosphorus	0.11	Silica	0.004	Iron	0.0027
Sulphur	0.11	Zinc	0.0025	Aluminum	0.0025
Fluorine	0.10	Copper	0.0004	Boron	0.0007
Barium	0.08	Tin	0.0002	Manganese	0.00036
Manganese	0.08	Bromine	0.0002	Zinc	0.00035
Nitrogen	0.03	Manganese	0.0001	Copper	0.00025
Strontium	0.02	Iodine	0.0001	Titanium	0.00009
Miscellaneous	0.47	Miscellaneous	0.0002	Miscellaneous	0.00015

Chemical substances of living things:

Water		60	75
Chemical substances		4.3	2.45
Organic compounds		35.7	22.5
Glucosides		6.2	18
Lipoids		11.7	0.5
Proteins		**17.8**	

NOTE: The figures represent percentages of the total components. The elements are listed in order of importance. The figures for the biosphere are taken from P. Thomas, as an average of the lithosphere (93%), hydrosphere (7%) and atmosphere (0.04%). The remaining figures, from G. Bertrand, refer to the average composition of the human body and of flowering alfalfa.

And so, taking into account only the simplest factors, we must agree that the difference between living and non-living matter, though clear enough, is not very important. It becomes much clearer as soon as we look at molecules rather than atoms. Indeed, it is so marked that at the beginning of the last century it was thought that the essential difference between life and matter was to be found on this level: that organic compounds, the specific and characteristic product of living things, formed a special group on which was based the mysterious power of life. In contrast to silicas and silicates, which between them make up 94 per cent of the lithosphere (felspar amounts to 57.7 per cent of this figure, and quartz to 12.6 per cent), the world of carbon, with its glucosides, lipoids and proteins, represents 90 per cent of living substance, if we ignore water, which alone constitutes two-thirds of the organism: animals differ from plants only in that they favor proteins and lipoids, while plants abound in glucosides.

The difference between life and its environment, between organic and physical chemistry, appeared so obvious and indisputable that Wöhler in 1828 alarmed scientists and philosophers by synthesizing urea from two chemical compounds, ammonium sulphate and potassium isocyanate. A door had opened through which were to pass all Liebig's syntheses, and above all those of Berthelot: biochemistry is now hardly more than a chapter of organic chemistry. Instead of the unbridgeable gap imagined by our forefathers, there remains little more than a vague line of demarcation: the true border is elsewhere, for a frontier does not cease to exist just because a mistake has been made over its precise location.

Structure

Can we distinguish life, even if motionless, even if dead, from inert matter? Yes, the man in the street will say, together with the paleontologist, who has never actually found a living creature in all the sedimentary layers he has examined.

Life can generally be recognized by its exterior form, and always by its internal organization. A statue differs from a corpse because the mineral substance of a statue is homogeneous, in complete contrast to that of a corpse. If, instead of a statue, we consider a very complex clockwork made of innumerable cogs, we soon see that the substance of these cogs, if of good quality, is also homogeneous, while the smallest piece of a corpse is made up of a number of specialized cells. Even on the microscopic level, we find everything diversified and subtly organized, and with the mark of its history and origin plainly shown, since it was built from the inside out; while the statue or the clockwork were made from the outside. Living creatures, even after their death, are the fruit and result of their own particular history, while the statue emerges from the history of the person who modeled it.

We can say, then, that life differs from inert matter merely by force of its structure, and paleontologists, when they find a fossil, do not bother to examine its chemical composition—which no longer means anything—to see whether it was once alive, but its internal structure. No confusion is possible with a crystal, perfectly homogeneous inside, which is also built up from the outside; the paleontologist can recognize even a part of a once-living thing from the still-visible traces of its activity and that of the organism of which it was a part. The difficulty begins when the fragment is so small that it is impossible, even with the wildest guesswork, to place it in its parent organism. Many ancient species are completely unknown to us, and it is quite possible that a certain number of fragments have not been recognized as coming from living things just because no one has discovered their function or their place in a living or fossil organism. This is seen especially in the very first living creatures (cf. Chapter 6), whose forms seem to have been simpler and whose remains are badly preserved. A special class has been set up for them by cautious paleontologists: that of the *stromatoliths,* a kind of waiting room out of which no living thing is allowed to emerge without its civic status completely guaranteed. When a paleontologist tells us, then, that such and such a fragment belongs to a living creature, we can have full confidence in him.

However, organization is not by itself a direct proof of life: in order to be absolutely sure, we must see it working. And here we come to its essential characteristic, its behavior.

Behavior

When studying life, it is essential, as Comte has pointed out, to take that point of view by which we will be able to explain details in terms of the whole, as opposed to physics and chemistry, which explain the whole by the parts. A living thing is a whole, which Kant has summed up in an admirable definition: it is "its own cause and effect." In other words, it acts, and the aim of its action is itself; it works for itself and constructs itself.

At the end of the last century, biologists were still enthusiastic over the discovery of the cell, and considered it the prototype of all living things. This belief, which betrays its age, reflects a time when the discovery of physiology, and of the hormones in particular, had not yet shown us how complex an organism is, and how such complexity is only equaled by its unity. It is not the separate cogs but their meshing that lets us understand a clock. We must realize that a living thing forms a whole, and that it does not exist apart from this whole. If a worm when chopped into pieces can form a new worm out of each piece by regeneration, it is still not a living thing we see but its fragments, which are thus reorganizing their structure and growing whole once more. Life is a whole formed out of disparate elements that have not come together by chance, and we cannot conceive of an organism composed entirely out of marble, iron or glucose: diversity is essential to it, and the secret of life is its ability to hold together and direct this diverse assemblage. The unity of a living thing transforms this diversity into specialization, and the different activities are organized into complementary functions. Every living thing has a certain awareness of itself, of the organization it consists of, of its needs and the dangers it faces, and its reactions are consequential to this; here is the real and profound difference between life and matter, however similar they may be elsewhere. The activities that show that this unity is working are the characteristics of life. These are feeding, reproduction and, above all, spontaneity.

Food is necessary to living things because they are not fueled like machines but take their energy from their own substance. To replace this energy they must take nutriments out of the environment and change them into their substance.

The crystal "nourishes itself," but not by assimilation: it lays hold of molecules identical to its own that have reached the right place through Brownian motion, and fixes them there by a combination of the forces involved. Fire nourishes itself by growing like a chemical reaction among the materials it encounters. But the growth of a crystal is too external, and that of fire too impersonal, to be compared with that of life.

Living things, however un-self-conscious they may be, experience the need for food and, whether by instinct or by intelligence, will do anything to satisfy this ineluctable necessity. An animal eats its food, chews it and reduces it to its smallest components by means of its teeth and the digestion that takes place in its stomach and intestines, where chemical bases break down whatever has escaped the acids. When the food has been broken down as far as possible and no longer has any resemblance to the form it had when still part of a living being, but has been reduced to a shapeless mass, it is assimilated by the organism through its intestinal villosities. Digestion consists in putting the necessary elements at the disposition of the organism, and in order that they may be more fully and

completely at its disposition, all trace of their former function is removed: they are turned into building blocks for
the monument that the organism is going to construct.
These elements reach the liver, where they are stored and
released into the bloodstream according to need; the blood
carries them through the body; and each cell draws from
this liquid, which, continually replenished, offers the necessary nutriments and carries away the waste products of the
cell, which would otherwise accumulate dangerously.

Life makes use of inert matter, masters and assimilates
it, but gets rid of it when it loses its usefulness. Let us take
a precise example.

We know that nearly all the nutriments which provide
the body with energy must pass through the liver, where
they are adapted for use. Now, in a mouse weighing five
grams and living at a temperature of 18°, the total energy
contained in the liver is about two calories. Such a mouse
expends rather more than fourteen calories a day. It follows that the constituents of the liver, taken as a whole,
must be renewed more than seven times a day, and if we
accept that not everything is renewed at the same speed,
some parts must be renewed at a much greater speed.

If instead of considering the whole liver we only study
its fats, we find that they are renewed at least twenty-
eight times every twenty-four hours; thus most of the fats
in the liver are kept there for less than an hour. This in-
terval diminishes as the temperature of the atmosphere
falls, or as the expenditure of energy increases.

In spite of such internal disruptions, life continues its
work, the organism remains the same and its delicate

mechanisms function unchanged. Nonetheless each of these mechanisms is closely connected to all the others, and can only function properly if they do: so much so that if any part fails, all the others are affected, and work in order to set it right. Every part of a living being is in mutual dependence with every other, and this unity is really the characteristic feature of life.

This extraordinary unity is also shown in reproduction and in the process of growth to adult size. Living matter does not have the stability of inert matter, that immovable tranquillity which can defy the centuries. Living things die, but on the other hand they can reproduce themselves, and through them life, always changing and always new, can travel across the ages. These new beings, so different from the adult form at the moment of their birth, construct themselves little by little in a remarkable harmony through a whole series of mechanisms, which it would take too long to describe here; and if a few monstrosities sometimes appear to disturb this delicate process, they show us how wrong we are not to be astonished by a harmony so normal that we are only surprised by its absence.

Spontaneity

Life's most obvious characteristic is its spontaneity: a living thing acts independently to complete or to safeguard its unity. But how can we demonstrate this spontaneity? How can we distinguish a spontaneous act from the result of an internal mechanism? If I did not know how an alarm clock works, would I not be justified in speaking of its spontaneity when, all of a sudden, I hear it ring?

When we carry out some voluntary action after thinking about it, without being forced to it by an exterior cause, this act is spontaneous. Spontaneity is not destroyed by some exterior stimulus that does not immediately cause the action: the noise of the alarm clock may be the cause of my waking up, but it has nothing to do with the fact that I then get up. By a psychological study I can thus convince myself of the spontaneity of this or that of my actions. But when a living thing is in question, I know too little about it to tell whether an action, apparently spontaneous, does or does not depend on external causes that escape me: it may after all be an automatism that copies life.

We must therefore experiment carefully and, instead of waiting for spontaneous reactions, try to provoke them. If the stimulus we apply is a natural one, or at least does not destroy natural processes, it may well be that the result corresponds perfectly to the cause and that there is nothing in the reaction that is not to be found in the action, except for changes imposed by the structure of the "patient": thus a watch will convert into motion the energy it has obtained from being wound up.

If I do something to a living thing that tends to destroy or diminish it, the reaction becomes clearer, and I can easily distinguish the effect of the stimulus and the action of the living organism. If inert matter is burned, the parts not touched by the red-hot iron will be only indirectly affected, either by conduction or by radiation. The reaction will not spread beyond limits determined by physics;

yet it is not physics that explains the flight of the animal, but spontaneity, thanks to which the animal tries, consciously or unconsciously, to escape being burned.

The best way to show the spontaneity of a living thing is to hurt it, which is why biology usually speaks of sensitiveness rather than spontaneity. Living things are sensitive because they are spontaneous, and it is in sensitiveness that spontaneity appears most clearly. Sensitiveness is thus native to any organism, because it presupposes unity and dynamism, together with a certain consciousness of self and of the usefulness of flight, in which the whole organism collaborates. It is found wherever there is life, for the smallest bacteria can adapt themselves to a new environment, which suggests that though at first they find the environment unsuitable, nevertheless they discover how to live in it.

In this way a whole series of characteristics distinguish life from matter. If an organism breathes, reproduces itself, grows and reacts spontaneously, we cannot doubt that it is alive; indeed we have only to make sure that it carries out one of these functions. The central and characteristic point is its dynamic unity, and all its acts are significant insofar as they allow this unity to be understood.

In practice, such a differentiation is not always easy, however clear the theoretical distinctions may be: hesitation and even mistakes are quite possible. That there is a gap between life and matter no one will deny, but there is little agreement about its size or about the possibility of bridging it. This account would be incomplete if we did not mention here the illusions of those who thought to have bridged this gap, and the hopes that still remain to us of doing so.

The Illusions

In antiquity, and until recently, when the complexity of living matter had not yet been revealed by the microscope or by biochemistry, too much attention was paid to the exterior form, and too often a resemblance was mistaken for identity.

Certain insects when touched freeze into an attitude that, when they are on a bush, makes them look like twigs. Reading the paper on xylophytes written by Kircher—whose scientific reputation is otherwise incontestable—it seems probable that it was these insects that made him believe he had seen the transformation of a plant into an animal.

Ulysses Aldovrandi, who died in the first years of the seventeenth century, tells us a fabulous story, with drawings to illustrate it. Barnacles are small crustacea whose shape is vaguely like that of a duck or goose, and they were thought to be the fruit of a tree. In his great *Natural History*, Aldovrandi draws a tree on the seashore whose fruit are barnacles and under which swim barnacle geese, those wild geese that migrate to our coasts in winter from polar regions. That the tree produced barnacles was never doubted by him, for his main point was that when these barnacles fell into the water they developed and turned into geese. A series of drawings shows us all the transitions necessary to produce a normal barnacle goose.

Let us proceed immediately to the twentieth century. Did not Stéphane Leduc commit a like blunder, in a series of famous experiments? Here they are, described by the author himself in 1906:

> While trying to stimulate the physical conditions of life, I made some artificial seeds composed of a third of copper sulphate, two-thirds of sugar and water; I sowed these seeds in an artificial plasma of water, gelatine, potassium ferrocyanide and a little salt; the seed surrounded itself with a membrane of copper sulfate, permeable to water and salts but impermeable to the sugar, which produced a strong osmotic pressure within, by reason of which the seed swelled, germinated and grew, putting out rhizomes and roots and then vertical stalks, which grew to a height of thirty centimeters; these stalks, branched or unbranched, sometimes carried lateral leaves; they had terminal organs in the shape of spines, globes, seed caps, tendrils and so forth. These growths had a circulatory system in which, like sap in plants, the sugar and the membranogenous substance rose to a height of thirty centimeters. When a stalk was broken during growth, the broken pieces came together and joined up; a scar was formed and growth began again. These growths were very sensitive to every kind of physical and chemical influence, to heat and cold, differences of concentration and chemical poisons.

In this experiment, which really belongs to the lighter side of physics, some people have seen a synthesis of life, and we wonder if Leduc himself did not sometimes take those words "artificial seeds" seriously.

But the most famous of these illusions, that of Haeckel,

comes from the end of the last century. This militant evolu-
tionist believed so deeply in the great chain of being that
he invented forms as missing links. The gap between matter and life seems especially to have stimulated his inventive
mind, and he came to picture a living creature so simple
that it could hardly be distinguished from matter; so little
differentiated that it could be thought of as the origin of
both animal and vegetable life: the moneron.

This little creature was imagined as a kind of amoeba
without a nucleus. Since the amoeba was then thought of
as a cell of protoplasmic jelly with an internal nucleus, we
can easily see that it was hard to imagine a living thing
simpler or more rudimentary.

"They are," said Haeckel, "very small living corpuscles,
which, properly speaking, do not merit the name of organism. Indeed, when we talk of living creatures, the word
organism refers to a living body composed of organs, of
dissimilar parts that, like the parts of an artificial machine,
are geared to one another and work together in order to set
the whole in motion. However, in these last few years we
have recognized that the monera are organisms that are
not composed of organs; they are composed of a matter
that is simple, homogeneous and without structure. When
alive its body is no more than a mucilaginous clot, mobile
and shapeless, composed of a carbonaceous albuminoid. It
is impossible for us to imagine any organism that could be
simpler or more rudimentary."

Then, in 1878, Thomas Huxley fished up from the deep
sea, between four and eight thousand feet down, a kind of
mucilaginous jelly that corresponded more or less with

Haeckel's moneron, since it was amorphous and without a nucleus. Evidently it was one of those mysterious and primitive creatures that still exist as they did during the dawn of the world, in the great melting pot of the oceanic depths.

Among those who followed Haeckel, the news brought about an explosion of enthusiasm, and Huxley could do no less than dedicate this marvelous moneron to the German scientist: he baptized it *Bathybius Haeckeli* (*bathybius*, the dweller in the deeps). Haeckel had triumphed, and in all his works on evolution this newcomer was given the principal place. The biochemists, however, going to work with less enthusiasm and a more critical spirit, soon came out with a different answer, and Huxley himself, at the congress of the British Association of Science held at Sheffield in 1879, confessed his mistake with typically British humor:

> The President, in an early part of his address, alluded to a certain thing—I hardly know whether I ought to call it a thing or not—of which he gave you the name Bathybius, and he stated, with perfect justice, that I had brought the thing into notice; at any rate, indeed, I christened it, and I am, in a certain sense, its earliest friend. For some time after that interesting Bathybius was launched into the world, a number of admirable persons took the little thing by the hand, and made very much of it, and I thought my young friend Bathybius would turn out a credit to me. But I am sorry to say, as time has gone on, he has not altogether verified the promise of his youth. In the first place, he could not be found when he was wanted; and in the second place, when he was found, all sorts of things

were said about him. Indeed, I regret to be obliged to tell you that some persons of severe minds went so far as to say that he was nothing but simply a gelatinous precipitate of slime, which had carried down organic matter.

Whereas Huxley thus abandoned his discovery, Haeckel passionately defended the reality of this organism, whose place was so fundamental to his system, and he never abandoned it.

The Hopes

Let us leave aside these ingenuous ideas and draw up the balance sheet of the scientific hopes that remain to us.

After the belief that chemistry divided the world into two distinct parts, that of living and of non-living matter, with an unbridgeable gap dividing organic and inorganic chemistry, a wild hope sprang up among scientists when Wöhler synthesized urea in 1828. Biological analysis was still new, organisms did not appear very complex and during the second half of the nineteenth century everyone thought that the day of the great synthesis could not be far off.

This hope has disappeared, or at least no longer seems realizable in the near future, because the chemistry of living matter has shown itself to be extraordinarily complex and delicate. An organism is not made up of a mere ten or twelve simple substances: the number is already greater than twenty, and the list is still growing. Vitamins have been discovered, together with hormones, and followed by the transporters of hydrogen and all the processes of oxygen combustion. How is all this to be organized?

Some have tried to simplify the problem by saying that it is enough to construct the first cell from which life developed; but this makes the biologist smile, for he already sees a perfect organism in this cell, with all its characteristics, its qualities and its future defects, in short, its heredity. Undoubtedly it is easier to construct the adult form itself rather than to give this work to a microscopic cell that is left to itself immediately it is made. Life carries with it a remarkable dynamism and a future too well mapped out for us to hope to create any organism that has not already fulfilled its destiny and has nothing left to do in the world but maintain itself. We will have to look for the simplest adult organisms, and it is their synthesis that we must first attempt.

There are three stages in this program. The first is to study the organism to be reproduced, its form, structure and above all its chemical composition and the details of its constituents: glucosides, lipoids, proteins and the many vitamins and hormones. Once this inventory is complete, we will have to synthesize each of these substances one by one from their chemical elements. Then all that remains is to put everything together.

The first stage is still quite incomplete. New organic elements are being discovered every day among animals and plants, and the end does not seem to be in sight. Chemical formulae there are in plenty, but think of the number of hormones, for example, whose main constituents are still unknown!

The second stage is obviously much less advanced, but

progress is so quick in this field that we can allow ourselves considerable hope, as long as we remain patient.

The third stage, the putting together of the synthesized elements, is much the most difficult. From what we know of coacervation, certain mixtures of lipoids and proteins will automatically find a stable equilibrium; but this does not mean that we will be able to throw all the constituents of an organism into a test tube, in their right proportions, for the organism to reconstitute itself automatically.

Our task will be to construct the organism. We will have to build the complex edifices of the proteins, intermingled with those of the glucosides and lipoids, without forgetting the molecules of water and mineral salts. But will this first edifice stand when others are added to it; when we try to add diastase molecules, or hormones, will not the whole structure crumble? Even if we had all the time in the world to put the finishing touches to this delicate edifice, how could we stop all kinds of reactions from occurring? Moreover, for no detail to be left out of the reconstitution, these reactions would have to be vital ones, not those produced in dead bodies.

The complexity of the problem is apparent, and it is evident that the artificial synthesis of a living organism will not happen this year.

3 / In Search of Intermediate Stages

Since Pasteur's experiments, we no longer believe that biogenesis is either easy or normal, but rather that the gap separating life from matter is sharply defined and, unless the contrary can be proved, apparently unbridgeable. However, a certain number of recent discoveries specify or even restate the problem. They have been made on both sides of the gap, and on one hand deal with the infra-microbes, the viruses and bacteriophages, and on the other with the study and synthesis of organic compounds.

The Infra-Microbes

When Pasteur revealed the existence of microbes and convinced all his contemporaries of their importance, many scientists and enthusiasts armed themselves with microscopes in order to explore this new world.

Most of the time the problem was to single out the infectious diseases and discover the microbe responsible. It had to be shown that illness is not a variety of self-destruction of diseased tissue, but the product of living organisms, bacteria, and that these are not the result, as some had affirmed, but the cause or agent of the destruction of the tissues.

Pasteur and his disciples won remarkable success along these lines, but their opponents resisted every inch of the way, and were quick to announce their disbelief when they heard Ivanowski, in 1893, state that a disease of tobacco leaves, in every appearance comparable to bacterial infections, was caused by a living organism impossible to isolate, a "filter-passing virus." It was called thus because its infinitesimal size allowed it to pass through every filter that was used to stop it. Can a living thing be so small that it is invisible through the microscope and can pass through every filter? Many scientists, even those who followed Pasteur, thought this was going a bit far.

Discoveries

However, in 1908, and definitively in 1915, François d'Hérelle discovered a very curious phenomenon while studying bacterial cultures. When they are numerous enough, these bacteria are seen under the microscope as a continuous layer, of darkish color. On certain of these preparations, small white borders appeared and grew larger; the bacteria disappeared progressively, without leaving the slightest trace, and the microscope was unable to reveal anything within the borders.

D'Hérelle thought that this might well be a bacterial parasite that digested them and remained invisible because it was so much smaller than they were. To demonstrate this, he undertook a series of experiments to show that he was really dealing with corpuscles and that these corpuscles were alive.

Using a platinum wire, he touched the preparation inside the white borders: a small drop remained on the tip of the wire, and this he dabbed elsewhere in the dark expanse of bacterial growth. Soon a small clear patch appeared there, grew and formed a typical white border. The minute drop at the tip of the platinum wire had thus been enough to provoke the appearance of a white border: but was this because of the liquid it was composed of, or because of corpuscles inside the liquid?

To answer this question, let us take a culture of bacteria in which we add a minute trace of this liquid, a hundred thousandth of a cubic millimeter, which we will dilute in order to spread it over the entire culture. If we are dealing with a plain liquid, its efficacy will diminish as it is diluted, but the entire surface of the culture will be affected in the same way. If we are dealing with corpuscles, their strength will not be modified by the dilution, but, at the concentration we have reached, they will become dispersed and the white borders will develop around certain definite places, leaving the rest untouched. Since this is indeed the case, we can conclude that the infection has been caused by corpuscles. We can also use this method to count them if we know the concentration we started with or how much we have diluted the droplet; this is the classic method for counting microbes, with the difference that here the dilution must be much greater because the corpuscles are very small and are counted in millions.

If the problem of bacteriophages was solved, it was also suddenly seen as part of a much larger problem, that of the viruses, which seemed more and more to include the bacteriophages. Indeed the main point of difference, among many points in common, is that the bacteriophages attack bacteria, while viruses attack plants or animals much larger than themselves. From the medical point of view the difference is enormous, because viruses can cause fearful illnesses, while bacteriophages are useful in healing.

A list of all the known viruses would be immense. We can mention a few of the ones that attack man: those causing influenza, exanthematic typhus, measles, mumps, poliomyelitis, hydrophobia and the common cold; for domestic animals, the best known are aphthous fever, fowl pest, swine fever and so forth; for plants we find viruses that cause tobacco and potato mosaic, and those other diseases that attack potatoes and are called *degenerate* because they are not yet curable; these are only dealt with by using seed grown in the mountains, where the altitude prevents the virus from developing.

By methods similar to those used in studying bacteriophages, viruses have been studied: the results show that we are dealing with a unique group, similar enough so that research on one virus can help in learning about the others. All these creatures, which we can call by the general name of virus, are between ten and two hundred millionths of a millimeter; all are obligatory parasites, which cannot live or reproduce outside of living cells, whether of bacteria, animals or plants.

The Structure of Viruses

The advance of chemistry, together with that of microscopy, has brought together a surprising number of facts concerning viruses.

The first task for the biochemist was to analyze their composition. The major obstacle was their size: how can one be sure whether this tiny invisible creature is really in the test tube? All possible methods were used to isolate the virus: the ultracentrifuge, working at prodigious speeds above 100,000 revolutions a minute; fractional ultrafiltration; preferential absorption; the action of certain diastases; and so forth. Finally, the virus was open to chemical study.

The largest viruses, whose diameters are a hundred millionth of a millimeter or more, have a constitution more or less like that of bacteria, or even of higher organisms; they are formed from proteins with glucosides and lipoids. The proportion of these glucosides and lipoids is small enough, but their presence was proved to be essential when Rivers and Macfarlane tried to remove them but could only do so by profoundly altering the virus, which then lost its virulence and pathogenicity.

The smallest viruses, whose diameter is about a hundredth of a micron (ten millionths of a millimeter), have a much simpler constitution, and no doubt a much simpler physiology. They seem to be made up of nothing but nucleoproteins, from which they get their name of protein-viruses.

The first general conclusion we can draw is that the essential, omnipresent element in all viruses is nucleic acid. We could say that among all the elements that make up living matter this is the most "noble," the one that is always named first among the essential elements of every living creature. Nucleic acid forms a chain whose links are glucosides; these carry a purine or pyrimidine base and a molecule of phosphoric acid, which joins them to the next glucosides. The glucoside is a ribose with five carbon atoms, which have lost one atom of oxygen: it is thus called *ribodesose* or *desoxyribose*. Great importance has been placed on this minute chemical difference, since it was seen that only the desoxyribose or desoxyribonucleic acids formed the skeleton of the chromosomes and consequently are responsible for heredity, while the ribonucleic acids form the mitochondria and the microsomes and are absent from the nucleus except within the nucleoles.

Nucleic acids are not distributed by chance in viruses, either. Plant viruses only have ribonucleic acids; animal viruses and bacteriophages are formed basically of desoxyribonucleic acids, to which, in the largest species, ribonucleic acids are joined.

The importance of nucleic acids lies in the fact that they are closely connected with the synthesis and multiplication of proteins. Everything formed out of nucleic acids reproduces itself, sometimes independently of the cell, and the multiplication of cells themselves is primed by the thickening and dividing of the chromosomes.

With proteins we enter into a special and little-known world. Their complex structure, and the folding of their chains, lead us to believe that they were formed in a kind of mold with the help of diastases and, no doubt, of divalent metals. This "mold" can give birth either to the same kind of molecule or to a reverse and complementary one: the multiplication of chromosomes and mitochondria is of the first type, the production of antibodies is of the second. We discover in this way the proteins, the foundation of heredity and immunity.

When foreign protein enters an organism, it provokes a reaction; but it may also enter without opposition, as a virus does, and establish itself in its host's heredity. The same is true for "unclothed" viruses, ones that have lost their protein tunics and that become increasingly virulent as they avoid provoking antibody reactions or as they remain untouched by previously formed antibodies. The most dangerous viruses are those that introduce themselves without fuss and take control, sometimes insidiously through a kind of symbiosis, sometimes brutally by appropriating most of the host's proteins.

A colibacillus infected by a bacteriophage apparently suffers no change. Neither the consumption of oxygen nor the total expenditure of energy has altered; but the bacterium, which usually makes only ribonucleic acid, now replaces this by the characteristic desoxyribonucleic acid of the phage: soon the phage is controlling its host's protein synthesis, and the host is working almost entirely for the benefit of the parasite.

The Behavior of Viruses

Thanks to the electronic microscope, Penso has confirmed D'Hérelle's intuitions with remarkable photographs.

He has been able to film the attack of a bacteriophage on a bacterium.

The bacteriophage looks more or less like a nail. The electric charges in its point are attracted by the complementary charges found on the membrane of the bacterium. A certain number of these "nails" fix themselves on the bacterium and empty their desoxyribonucleic acid onto it, while the virus' ghost, its shell, remains in place.

Inside the bacterium the microscope can no longer make anything out, and for a few minutes the bacteriophage has disappeared. However, after the seventh minute, protein synthesis begins, and soon virus shells begin to take shape and to wait for their complement of nucleic acid. When this comes to occupy its place inside the shell, the bacteriophage is reconstituted, and its virulence reappears. In a few minutes the bacterium explodes and sets free a swarm of young bacteriophages. The whole drama has taken twenty minutes, during which each bacteriophage has given rise to more than a hundred new ones.

Again, sometimes the virus does not reconstitute itself but maintains itself in a state of provirus, not only inside the infected bacterium but also in the bacterium's descendants; clandestinely, or as a recessive, it can thus travel through several generations, and this opens new horizons for medicine and heredity.

Does the provirus—or, more exactly, the virus' nucleic acid—attach itself to a chromosome in order to be multiplied with it? But then can a gene be so different from a virus? Can the virus be a gene that has managed to detach itself and form a shell?

The study of the symbiotic life of viruses no doubt has many surprises in store for us. D'Hérelle opened up certain unexpected vistas. The bacteriophage, for example, can install itself in a certain kind of bacterium and remain there quite unperceived: only one in a million, or even less, of these bacteria will explode. If a new kind of bacterium appears, however, the domesticated virus regains its virulence.

According to D'Hérelle, our health must be connected with this symbiosis between bacteriophage and colibacillus. For example, a certain kind of bacteriophage will infect the colonies of colibacilli so numerous in the human large intestine, and found there in the first days after birth. Our resistance to contagious diseases will depend on the good or bad kind of bacteriophage that has first installed itself inside us. If this is so, the greatest service we can give our children is to supply them immediately upon birth with a selected bacteriophage that will be very active against most of the bacteria that attack us. It is true that a cure can become contagious if the convalescent transmits—to others who are falling prey to the same sickness—the bacteriophages that are beginning to conquer the bacteria inside him; but these bacteriophages, which have not become acclimatized within us, do not live long and are slowly eliminated by the ones already present. When a new contagion occurs we find ourselves again depending on the same bacteriophage that first installed itself within us.

In this way a number of viruses can live for a long time in symbiosis with other organisms that they could easily destroy if they were virulent. But the danger is always there: these viruses can be waked up and made virulent once more by means of ultraviolet radiation or any other kind of mutating agent. Cancerogenic substances have the same effect: does cancer therefore arise from the activation of a provirus?

Are Viruses Alive?

The problem of whether viruses are alive is complex and full of significance. If viruses are not alive, how can they be so closely related to bacteria? On the other hand, is it possible that everything necessary for life can be packed into such a minute size?

Above all, does the virus form itself and its descendants, or is it only the seed or catalyst that allows its host to create it? This last theory would mean that viruses stimulate the rapid formation of substances identical to their own. Since they would be incapable, as non-living particles, of assimilating and transforming matter into their own substance, the plants or bacteria that give rise to different viruses must contain already formed, or be able to form immediately, the different substances that characterize the virus. But mosaic virus, for example, can infect about fifty different plants, and maintain itself in identical fashion in all of them. How can fifty different plants manage to individualize this particular virus, with the same ease as they find in producing other ones? It is much more logical to admit that viruses are alive and that they are produced, not by the host, but at his expense; the contaminated plant provides suitable nourishment, which the virus assimilates, and which allows it to reproduce. The virus is as independent of its host as a mammalian egg is of the mother who carries it in her womb. It develops if the environment is suitable, but barring accidents, the environment does not modify its heredity.

The individuality of viruses is so clear-cut that we use it when isolating them; for example, true bacteriophages are not all equally active on certain kinds of bacteria, and successive cultures in the same medium will leave behind only the most active strains. Thanks to heredity, this individuality is kept by the descendants, and a virus that can act on some thirty kinds of plant will keep this capacity even if it has been parasitic on only one species for a long time.

When a species of virus invades a host, it takes possession; if a new species arrives, it finds the environment modified by the first occupant. If it is very different, it cannot install itself; if similar, it invades, and the two viruses multiply together. In their dispersed state they are capable of recombining among themselves, of becoming hybrids, as is were, for in this they follow Mendelian laws so closely that we already know the gentics of bacteriophages.

Another argument put forward by D'Hérelle in favor of bacteriophages being alive is their capacity of adaptation—to heat, for example. Every species can only live within definite limits of temperature. However, if the temperature is progressively raised by steps of one degree, then by steps of half a degree, and then by quarters of a degree, we can obtain strains that can live at some ten degrees above their previous critical temperature. Some may think that selection has operated to favor a strain originally hidden in the bacteriophage population, but this is not the case: if the temperature is raised in one step instead of in a number of steps, all the bacteriophages die, without exception. The resistance to temperature is thus a progressive adaptation of a living creature.

While the proofs that viruses are alive were thus accumulating, a sensational discovery stirred up the entire problem and set everything moving again: Stanley, in 1935, managed to crystallize the tobacco-mosaic virus. In reality, as X-ray diffraction studies demonstrate, we are not dealing with a genuine crystal with a regular disposition of molecules regularly repeated in three-dimensional space to form a characteristic solid. Instead, we have minute needles where the molecules are regularly arranged in two dimensions only: they are therefore paracrystals. Since then, real crystals seem to have been obtained in the form of small hexagonal tablets.

In spite of innumerable efforts, only a few viruses have been made to form crystals, among them the one responsible for stunting tomatoes, which gives beautiful crystals in the form of rhomboidal dodecahedrons, whose crystalline nature and fully three-dimensional structure cannot be doubted; and X-ray diffraction photographs indeed confirm the existence of a three-dimensional network whose basic pattern shrinks by dessication from 39.4 to 31.8 millionths of a millimeter.

Until recent years only a few plant viruses had been

crystallized. But in 1956, from California, came the news that the first animal virus, one of the agents of poliomyelitis, had been crystallized.

Crystallization is a process that seems to be a priori incompatible with life. It assumes that the small molecules that make up the crystal are all of the same size and shape, whatever that shape may be. If all the viruses of tobacco mosaic, or stunted tomato, are of exactly the same size and shape, we would have to conclude not only that such an organism is not very plastic, but also that it does not undergo a process of development, and possesses an immutable form from "birth."

This absence of development, however, is not a decisive argument against a virus being alive, since the same thing holds for butterflies, bees and all the insects, which only appear in their final form after their metamorphosis.

And yet those who do not wish to attribute life to viruses have good arguments. The smallness of viruses makes the presence of organized substances such as ferments impossible; sometimes even water is lacking. Viruses can be called alive, but they do not develop, do not breathe and, incapable of attacking even organic substances on their own, cannot live separated from the organisms they are parasitic on.

Partisans of the view that viruses are alive explain the problem quite differently. They say that viruses are living organisms that have degenerated through parasitism.

Bacteria are more or less normal living organisms. They are sometimes parasitic, but they can also live in an inert

environment. The bacterium causing tularemia, a sickness
of certain rodents that insects can transmit to man, often
installs itself in the interior of a cell, just like a virus,
though it otherwise behaves like an ordinary bacterium.
Certain of the rickettsia bacteria—small bacteria whose
size is sometimes as little as a hundred millionth of a millimeter—can live outside cells, and can even be cultivated
outside living matter, while others are obligatory parasites.

The largest of the viruses are similar in size to the
rickettsia bacteria, but are distinguished from them by an
even stricter parasitism and by the fact that they have already lost their digestive apparatus, the diastases. Every
kind of size and complexity is to be found, and by degrees
we arrive at the simplest of the viruses, which consists of
nothing but nucleoproteins.

Where shall we say, "Here is life," in this progressive
degeneration? Shall we make life depend on an ability to
live outside cells, and shall we then say that only certain
species of rickettsia bacteria are alive? Shall we link it to
the presence of diastases and the capacity to secrete them?
In this homogeneous group any definition risks being arbi-
trary, which is why most biologists class viruses as living
creatures. Viruses have lost complexity as organisms and
therefore have also lost the possibility of growth; they have
lost the power to produce the energy they require, but they
are skilled in making use of their host's energy to assimilate
the substances around them. As in many parasites, the re-
productive powers of viruses are pushed to the extreme, so
much so that assimilation is only used for reproduction.

This, in much simpler form, is also the stage of superior parasites, like the tapeworm.

This bird's-eye view has shown us various stages from indisputably living things to the very borders of matter. In passing from animals or plants to bacteria, the organism becomes simpler while its proportion of nucleoprotein and capacity to reproduce increases. As we descend the scale among the viruses, this amount increases even more, to the point where nucleoproteins alone remain and show us the capacity for reproduction in its pure state.

Because of parasitism, the characteristics of life appear little modified, for the parasite takes advantage of the organism it inhabits, and we can say that it becomes part of the parasite's body, rather like a graft on a parent stock. All its actions and reactions take place in a living environment and cannot be achieved outside it. The virus nourishes itself, but the actual digestion is done by the host, and the virus limits itself to assimilation. It is spontaneous or sensitive, since it has been found that bacteriophages find their host-bacteria by chemotaxis. It multiplies itself with prodigious speed, and its heredity remains constant over generations. We can therefore admit that the characteristics of life, while being much modified by parasitism, are to be found in the virus, and so it is not unlikely that viruses are alive.

But whether alive or not, it is still true that viruses occupy an intermediate zone between life and matter, and the fact that we cannot say with certainty that they are alive puts them even more definitely in this uncertain zone. If viruses are alive, they bridge a good part of the gap; if they are not, they bridge nearly all of it, since there is so little difference between the largest among them and the various kinds of rickettsia bacteria, some of which are almost indistinguishable from viruses.

Biochemical Syntheses

While living things grow smaller under the eye of the microbiologists, an immense program of research is renewing the status of organic chemistry and investigating the various substances found in the organism.

We have come a long way since Wöhler first synthesized an organic substance! Liebig and Berthelot have become famous in this new field. Synthetic chemistry has now reached such a degree of perfection that a substance whose formula is completely known is not far from being synthesized; and on the other hand, many syntheses have been accomplished for which a natural model did not exist.

The work is long and arduous. Suppose we are studying glucose. First we must isolate it, purify it and examine all its properties: hardness, density, appearance and so forth. An elementary analysis shows that it contains as many carbon atoms as oxygen, and twice as many hydrogen atoms; so it will have a formula of the type $(CH_2O)_n$. But what is the size of n? Different methods will reveal the exact weight of the molecule and leave us in no doubt that we are dealing with $C_6H_{12}O_6$. But our task is not finished, for hundreds of substances may have this over-all formula, and every hypothesis must be examined to find how these twenty-four atoms are attached to one another. This last work is the longest, and many hypotheses are not provable. When at last the formula is completely known in all its principal variants, and when no obscurity remains, the synthesis can be tried, and will sooner or later succeed.

Glucose, however, is one of the simplest substances in biochemistry; the problem becomes more complex when we start on proteins, particularly the nucleoproteins, which, as we have seen, play so large a part in the composition of chromosomes and of protein viruses.

Nucleoproteins can form enormous molecules, with molecular weights of about 500,000. While their purification is much harder than that of glucose, it is possible to give an over-all formula for them. But how are all these atoms arranged? Already we have managed to detach quite a large portion from this immense molecule, in the shape of nucleic acid. The molecular weight of nucleic acid reaches 1,300, but this figure is still small besides the 400,000 or 500,000 of the total molecule.

However splendid the results of our analyses and syntheses, they look somewhat feeble when compared to their model, the living organism, and the chemist can only feel that he is not yet competent to deal with something at once so complex and so fragile.

But the size of molecules that have already been synthesized is remarkable. In artificial rubbers, for example, starting with acetylene and going on to chloroprene, chemists have succeeded in polymerizing the latter by heat or ultraviolet rays into macromolecules whose molecular weight reaches 300,000. In spite of its size, however, such a molecule is much too simple and too homogeneous for us to consider its synthesis a big step toward the synthesis of life.

From Molecules to Viruses

Another part of the problem consists in searching for molecules in nature comparable to viruses, even if only in size.

Here we are at a scale of a thousandth of a micron, or a millionth of a millimeter. The ordinary microscope, it will be remembered, cannot distinguish objects smaller than two hundred millionths of a millimeter. *Bacillus prodigiosus* is very large, up to 7,500; rickettsias are about 300, while one of the largest viruses, that of vaccine, measures one hundred and seventy-five millionths of a millimeter. We may remember in passing that a hydrogen atom measures one ten-millionth of a millimeter.

The place of viruses is thus well defined, and we find them in all sizes between 200 and 10. The most interesting ones for our present purposes are those at 10, especially the staphylococcus bacteriophage S^{13} and the virus of aphthous fever, though unfortunately neither of these is well known chemically. At this size, if we assume that the entire particle forms one molecule, its molecular weight would be around 400,000. If virus vaccine was a molecule, its weight would be about 2 billion 300 million, and if *Bacillus prodigiosus* were one also, it would weigh nearly 200 trillion.

Among the commonest chemical substances, water has a molecular weight of 18, carbon dioxide one of 44, glucose one of 180, saccharose one of 342; and so forth. Certain molecules are much more voluminous, especially those of proteins, among which are found giant molecules such as egg albumin (weighing 40,000), horse hemoglobin (weighing 69,000) and above all, various hemocyanins: this copper-based pigment, which takes the place of hemoglobin among molluscs, weighs over a million, and one kind has even been found at 6,700,000.

The size of certain of these molecules has been measured. Egg albumin measures 0.6 by eighteen millionths of a millimeter, while hemoglobin measures 0.6 by twenty-eight millionths. The largest known hemocyanin molecule measures thirteen by fifty-nine millionths.

We can say that there is no difference in size and volume between living molecules and the largest organic molecules; the smallest living things are smaller than the largest molecules. And at this point we may take hope; we can already synthesize larger and larger organic molecules, and the progress of chemistry allows us to see the distant or, who knows, the not so distant day when we shall be able to make protein molecules as large as those of the smallest living organisms.

The Synthesis of Life

Essential though they may be in present-day research, the problems we have just looked at advance only slightly our thinking about the origins of life.

Let us admit that viruses are alive, and that the distance between matter and life is only the distance separating molecules of nucleoprotein from protein viruses; the possibility of the one turning into the other will not resolve the problem of how life started, since all these viruses, even the most complex, are obligatory parasites and can only live inside a living organism. This organism must therefore already be alive to act as host to the virus, and the problem of its origin remains unsolved: a living organism can prepare the way for a virus, but a virus cannot prepare the way for a living organism.

We can, of course, imagine that the first living organisms were special kinds of viruses, of which present-day viruses give us only a very poor notion; but then we are dealing in pure speculation. Even more, we go against the law of orthogenesis if we think that a parasite will regress down exactly the same path that life evolved upward on, and reproduce the original form, even when its function was quite different. This supposition is not defensible.

But let us return to the problem of artificially synthesizing life as we see it today. If size were the only consideration, we might not be far from success. Moreover, viruses break into their separate parts in order to multiply, and the elements forming these parts do not seem to be outside our power of synthesis. But life is not a simple matter of size or shape.

We are in fact a long way from our goal: a simple fact will demonstrate this. Toward the end of 1955 all the newspapers, even the more discriminating ones, announced nothing less than the synthesis of life, by two Americans, Fraenkel-Conrad and Williams. In reality, these two scientists had succeeded in disintegrating viruses by chemical means, so that these viruses thereupon lost their virulence: and certain of them reconstituted themselves into their former state when the culture medium was brought back to its normal pH level. This, at least, is what their virulence

ORGANISMS AND MOLECULES

	Molecular Weight	Diameter (in millimicrons)
Bacillus prodigiosus	173,000,000,000	750
Rickettsia:		
Common	11,000,000,000	300
Small	400,000,000	100
Virus:		
Vaccine	2,300,000,000	175
Tobacco mosaic	43,000,000	280/15
Poliomyelitis	700,000	12
Aphthous fever	400,000	10
Bacteriophage:		
Staphylococcus S^K	300,000,000	90
Megatherium	23,000,000	38
Staphylococcus S^{13}	400,000	10
Molecule of hemocyanin:		
Busycon	6,700,000	59/13.2
Rossia	3,316,000	64/8
Octopus	2,800,000	
Palinurus	446,000	
Molecule of erythrocruorine in the earthworm	2,990,000	
Molecule of Edestin	309,000	
Molecule of Hemoglobin	69,000	28/0.6
Molecule of Ovalbumin	42,100	18/0.6
Molecules: Synthetic (artificial rubber)		
Polychloroprene	300,000	
Polyoxyethylene	100,000	

NOTE: The table shows comparative sizes of the smallest living organism with the largest molecules in organic chemistry. The diameters in millionths of a millimeter are quoted from Stanley, with the two figures for the molecule's length and width added afterward. Most of the molecular weights are also quoted from Stanley, though recent photographs with the electron microscope have shown that aphthous fever virus has a diameter of between 20 and 32. For living organisms we are not dealing with a true molecular weight, but with the weight a molecule of this size would have.

and their appearance under the electron microscope seems to show. However, Gierer and Schramm believe that virulence can be transmitted merely by means of nucleic acids. If this is so, can we be sure that the viruses were really reconstituted?

Whatever the case may be, this experiment was remarkable in that it showed that we can interfere in the life of a virus with delicacy and precision. However, the way this experiment was presented must make us both cautious and even a little skeptical.

Is it because we hope for so little that we consider this result a great victory? Or is it, more simply, that journalists consider the problems of biogenesis so uninteresting that they think only an announcement of the synthetic creation of life worthwhile?

4 / The Philosophical Problem

The aim of philosophy being to understand, or at least to try to understand, we must confess that it has its work cut out in explaining the origin of life. The problem is this: we have found that there is not only a difference between matter and life, but a veritable chasm. Yet everyone agrees that this chasm, even if we cannot cross it today, must once have been crossed for life to appear on the earth.

Two philosophical attitudes—two lines of thought— have been taken toward this problem: materialism and spiritualism. The first says that the gap was crossed because, with luck, it cannot be as hard as all that to cross. The second says that the gap is too wide to be crossed in this way, that it is normally uncrossable and that only mind could have led matter toward life and allowed the great step to be taken.

Materialism

This tradition, which does without the intervention of mind, has two ways of dealing with the problem, according to whether the gap between matter and life is thought to be easy or difficult to bridge.

The "mechanists" usually postulate an immense gap between matter and life, which can only be bridged with great difficulty; they base their theories on Pasteur. However, if it is true that the gap was crossed by the first living things, then it is not impassable; and since the action of a Mind can hardly be invoked, that of some happy coincidence must be.

Lucretius, for instance, imagined atoms moving uniformly and continuously in the void. Sometimes they deviated minutely from their course, enough to cause numerous encounters: many of these had no result, but a certain number bore fruit. In this way the various objects that furnish our universe were constructed, together with living beings themselves. Moreover, since the earth still engenders a certain number of creatures under our very eyes, what must her power and fertility have been in her first youth! But the poet is not attempting to paint an idyllic scene of the world's dawn. Since the question was not evolution, but the appearance of different species, the great difficulty was to show how not only eggs but mammals had been formed; whatever the difficulty, some explanation had to be found, or the theory would not be coherent. Still, what was the earth not capable of producing in her youth?

> I return to the time when the world was young, when the earth was still soft, and I will tell what creations she decided to give birth to for the first time on the shores of light, and to entrust to the gusty winds.

First the earth brought forth every kind of plant and

springing verdure, covering the hills and all the plains; the green fields shone with flowers; then the various kinds of trees started on their race of growth through the air, unbridled and unreined. And, as feathers, hair and bristles are the first to grow on the limbs of birds and beasts, so the young earth put forth herbs and bushes and then created mortal things, which were born in great numbers, in many ways by different means. For animals cannot have fallen from the sky, nor can the beasts of the earth have crawled out of the deep sea: it is right then that the earth has received the name of mother, since from her all things have come. And even now many animals issue from the earth, formed by the rains and the heat of the sun: why should we then be surprised if larger and more numerous animals were born at a time when the earth and sky were still in their youth?

First those with wings, the various birds, hatched out of their eggs in the springtime, as nowadays grasshoppers leave their smooth shells of their own accord in summer, to find life and food. Then it was that the earth began to give birth to mortal things, for the fields then were warm and damp, and wherever a suitable place was found, in that place there grew wombs fixed to the earth by roots; and when their term had come and these wombs were opened by the efforts of the newborn, who were eager to leave the damp and find the open air, Nature turned the veins of the earth toward them and urged a juice like milk into their mouths; and in the same way now every woman, after she has given birth, is filled with sweet milk because all her nourishment flows to her breasts. The earth gave food to its children, and the fleecy grass provided a soft bed. But the youth of the world produced neither hard frosts, nor great heat, nor over-violent winds; for everything grew and came to its strength in equal measure.

Yet again, then, the earth well merits this name of mother that she has received, since by herself she created the human race and at the right times every animal that ranges and gambols over the mountains, and all the birds in their different forms. But since her fecundity had to come to an end, the earth ceased giving birth, as women do when they are old.[1]

The advance of science makes Lucretius' hypotheses difficult to accept; even those who place the onus on chance hardly ask it to perform so much, but at most the creation of a bacterium or a blue alga, and they confess that even such an apparently unspectacular result demands what is in reality an extraordinary combination of circumstances. We must then consider the statistical probability of such an event taking place.

Lecomte du Noüy has strongly criticized this appeal to chance.[2] In order to show that it is impossible to produce even a simple molecule of nucleoprotein, by these means, let alone a living thing, he has simplified the problem and made it real. He assumes, according to the calculations of C. E. Guye, that such a molecule can have a degree of dissymmetry amounting to 0.9; and for simplicity he supposes that it is composed of 2,000 atoms of only two different kinds—carbon and hydrogen, for example. These atoms are then likened to black and white balls that must be shaken together and let fall until chance combines them in the right

---

[1] *De rerum natura* v. 780–827.

[2] See his *Human Destiny* (New York: New American Library).

pattern. He also imagines, in order to hasten matters, that this shaking up—which must alter the entire arrangement and produce a new pattern, also the effect of pure chance— can be done in less than a second, rather than in several minutes, that indeed it can be done five hundred billion times a second. For molecules with 0.9 dissymmetry to form themselves into a volume equal to that of the terrestrial globe would require on average not less than 10^{243} billion years, i.e. a number with 253 digits. This number, compared to which "astronomical numbers" lose significance, is so far beyond the power of our imagination that it is really meaningless. We can thus say—and here no one will contradict Lecomte du Noüy—that an event so unlikely to occur is really impossible.

We think that this conclusion—the impossibility of life appearing by chance—is correct, but we have the right and even the duty to ask if these black and white balls are proper analogies for atoms. We must not forget that atoms have valences and are not indifferent to how they are placed; nor that in nature atoms are never isolated except momentarily, and that the first shaking up, however it be done, would lead to the construction of various molecules most of which would remain in existence, unless a force stronger than that of mere chance came to dissociate them: the potentialities of carbon uniting with almost anything, by means of its four valences, are nearly unlimited. By trying to simplify a problem and make it mathematically soluble, we risk finding an answer that no longer has anything to do with the problem.

Must we say that nothing is proved? No, for in reality the problem is even more complicated and the chances much smaller. The atoms of carbon, hydrogen, nitrogen and so forth already make up very stable molecules—for instance, those of carbon dioxide—and the first problem is to dissociate them; the second is to rearrange them according to the new plan.

We shall examine in the next chapter certain theories concerning sources of energy that could accomplish this in the primeval world; but this energy still has to be applied in the right place, and we must not believe that the expected synthesis will occur merely because it is thermodynamically easier. It would be naïve to imagine a car driving itself to California, though the engine worked and there was enough gasoline; and it is no less naïve to think that ultraviolet rays, for example, merely because they have the energy, will not only fabricate formaldehyde but will also polymerize its molecules to form first glucides and then nucleoproteins—as if this was the only possible direction to be taken, as if it represented the slope down which things naturally gravitate; whereas the difficulty is so great that man has been unable to resolve it in spite of all his knowledge. As Prenant has said with perfect justice, we are in the presence of a "lay miracle," but none of us will believe in it.

Dialectical materialism evades this miracle in admitting that, though at first sight difficult, the passage from matter to life is not so difficult when viewed dialectically.

Engels treated this problem in his *Dialectics of Nature,* an unfinished work that he wrote about 1880.

We have seen that at the beginning of the nineteenth century no distinction was made between what is organic and what is alive, but the difference between matter and life was thought to lie between organic and inorganic substances. The syntheses achieved by Wöhler, Liebig and Berthelot led biologists to change the place of the gap rather than to suppress it, and to class all organic matter with the non-living. Some people then got the impression that organic substances must be the intermediaries between matter and life, since they had so recently been considered as being alive. Engels' dialectical materialism continued, in spite of Pasteur, to hold that the passage from matter to life was possible by this already demolished route; that albumen is living matter, and that therefore its mere existence is enough for us to talk about life. How are these complex molecules synthesized? This problem is not faced, perhaps because it is thought too simple, or perhaps because the weight of scientific doubts would cause the dialectic bridge to collapse.

We saw how Haeckel, while looking for the simplest living things, postulated an unorganized stage, a stage where life is carried on by an agglomeration of proteins. Engels took over this notion (which fitted in so well with his own position), and took care not to cast doubts on *Bathybius Haeckeli*. Thus life, in spite of its dialectical dynamism, must have waited several millennia after forming these first creatures, which were organic if not organized, before it created a cell. But what can it have been waiting for, if not a lucky coincidence? And so we are back again, it seems, with the preceding theory.

But let Engels speak for himself. He is in the process of describing the various phases through which our planet has gone as it has cooled down:

If at last the temperature becomes steady over at least a considerable part of the surface and does not go beyond the limits between which albumen can survive, if the necessary chemical conditions are favorable, living protoplasm will be created. What the necessary chemical conditions are we do not yet know; but this is hardly surprising, since the chemical formula of albumen has not yet been established, since we do not even know how many kinds of chemically different albuminoids there are, and since some ten years ago we discovered that albumen, though completely without structure, exercises all the essential functions of life: digestion, elimination, movement, contraction, reaction to stimulations, and reproduction.

Millions of years probably passed before conditions allowed for the succeeding progress in which this shapeless albumen produced the first cell by forming a nucleus and a membrane. On this first cell, however, depended the morphological constitution of the organic world. From it, as all our paleontological data show, have developed innumerable species of cellular and non-cellular protistas, of which *Eozoon canadense* is the only example to come down to us, intact, and of which some developed little by little to form the first plants and others, the first animals.[3]

The position of modern dialectical materialists is not markedly different, except that they rely on bacteriophages

[3] *The Dialectics of Nature* (New York: International Publishers, 1940). We shall see in our last chapter the present state of paleontology, the data on the first living creatures that it supplies, and the reason why the Eozoon is no longer believed in. Haldane has a note on this subject: "*Eozoon canadense* is almost certainly not an organic product. However, there is every reason to consider this paragraph as being fundamentally correct."

and virus proteins instead of albumen. These minute organisms occupy exactly the same place in modern science as albumen did a century ago, and there are still arguments over whether they are alive or not. The very existence of this discussion, as Haldane and Prenant emphasize, shows that the passage from matter to life is not inconceivable, and that even contemporary studies in biogenesis will not come as a surprise; the great difficulty in the present state of science will be to ascertain whether new life has really appeared or not. As Haldane writes: "Nevertheless, the bare fact that some people argue with fury that such a virus is alive, and others argue with equal fury that it is not alive, while some say that there is no sense in making a distinction, indicates that not by any theoretical discussion, but by actual chemical technique, we have got the beginnings of a bridge between life and chemistry, even if we do not understand in the very least how a virus actually multiplies."[4]

And Prenant has decided that biogenesis not only occurred at the beginning, but that it has been going on ever since.

"Let us suppose," he writes, "that similar creatures appear in nature today by spontaneous generation, which, however, have not the distinct characteristics of filterable viruses or bacteriophages, but which are more like ordinary bacteria: we would know absolutely nothing about them. The hard thing would be, not to observe spontaneous generation, but to know when it happened. What would be exceptional for life would not be to appear but to maintain

[4] J. B. S. Haldane, *Marxist Philosophy and the Sciences.*

itself and evolve, above all in a world already occupied by living organisms that had originated previously: in the same way that it is exceptional, not for a mutation to appear, but for it to maintain itself and evolve. Thus all living creatures, both past and present, need not necessarily be descended from one single ancestor, a kind of protozoan Adam, but perhaps from a fairly large number of strains favored by chance among an infinite number of those that perished."[5]

Outside the realm of dialectics, where differences are subtly minimized, the passage from matter into life remains unexplained, and even scientifically inexplicable. We must fall back on chance, and it is here that we must look at the spiritualist theories, according to which mind is necessary to explain the impossible transition.

Spiritualism

Mind can intervene and bridge the gap either by its own immanent action, or by a transcendental command. Here are two very different ways of thinking, the first of which is based on continuity, the second on novelty. Both of them go back many centuries and have experienced their ups and downs, and both of them have been upheld by famous men, at least in the past, when philosophers seemed much preoccupied by this problem. These philosophers had to rely on the scientists of their epoch, who provided them with conclusions no one could question; and they asked themselves how the sudden appearance of life could be ex-

[5] Marcel Prenant, *Biology and Marxism* (New York: International Publishers).

plained and understood. Science has advanced since then, and we may smile at the naïveté of our predecessors; but philosophical thought, whether it be that of Lucretius or of Aristotle, always retains its force. This is because the laws and conditions of thought change no more than those of physics, and keep their value even if they have been used to explain a phenomenon that never happened.

THE EXPLANATION FROM IMMANENCE

As its name implies, the theory of immanence makes use of a Mind located, so to speak, in the very essence of matter.

St. Augustine, strongly influenced by the Stoics, thought that all material bodies were composed of matter and force. This dynamism—this *logos* placed by God in the heart of matter—was its ruler, and ruled it with most efficiency when it most imposed its will. It is this that gives life to animals and plants, that controls growth and fulfills it; it is thanks to this that the acorn becomes an oak and the egg a cock. It was called *logos spermatikos,* or the "seminal cause," because it is the seed of future life, and because all its power urges it toward that goal.

If we consider an egg or a seed, we could say that nothing distinguishes them from brute matter but their seminal cause, which awaits within them the right moment to begin development. This egg and this seed could not live if we deprived them of the conditions they wait for—warmth and humidity—and we can hasten their development by providing these conditions for them. We have their life in our hands. But—and it was this that struck St.

Augustine so forcibly—we cannot make this egg become anything except that which its seminal cause wants it to be; we cannot influence its future, only help or prevent its realization. These seminal causes are immutable, like the laws of nature or genetics; they are the laws of life.

> The elements of this corporeal world all have their own dynamism and their special quality which determine what they can or cannot accomplish, what they may or may not become.
>
> Let us consider a tree, magnificent in its vigor, its branches, foliage and fruit. It has sprung from its root, which the seed sent down into the earth, and it is from there that everything was shaped and diversified. This seed came from a germ: and so everything started by existing in germ, not of course the bodily size and bulk, but the dynamism and the causative power. How much more admirable and more important than mere size is this dynamism, enclosed in a minute seed that can use the surrounding moisture in the earth to change itself into this kind of wood, this reaching out of branches, this form and this verdure of its leaves. . . .![6]

These wonderful seminal causes cannot be the outcome of chance nor the work of man; but, in the days of the creation, God made each and every one of them and scattered them in the world where they awaited their proper time. They are innumerable, and to be found everywhere. Individuals, if they are fertile, contain in themselves the seminal causes of their descendants, and their role is

[6] *De Genesi ad litteram* v. 22.

to provide the proper environment in which these can develop.

These seminal causes exist not only in individuals but in nature, and the whole secret of biogenesis is to discover them and to make them develop in the right conditions, because, like the egg or the seed, they must patiently await such conditions before they can develop. The farmer who plows his field favors the seminal causes of weeds scattered in the soil. In the same way, meat contains within it the seminal causes of putrefaction, which wait until death brings about the proper conditions to develop. Bees do not engender their offspring, but the workers go searching through nature for the seminal causes of bees, which they bring back to their hive, where conditions for development are favorable.

Every time we see a new creature appear, we must conclude that its seminal cause has found the right conditions for development. From this viewpoint there was nothing surprising in the claim of scientists to be able to create life out of matter: matter had only "to be treated in the proper method, mixed in such and such a way, ground in such and such a way, or pounded in such and such a way. God is the only true origin of life, who created this power and placed it, still latent, in matter."

The first living thing appeared simultaneously with the conditions for living; and these first living beings can only have been very primitive organisms, since more advanced ones require the much more complex environment that only came later. In this way evolution was explained, or rather the progressive appearance of living things.

We again come across this dynamism—which Leibniz placed inside his *monads,* often hardly distinguishable from seminal causes—in Bergson's *élan vital.* This élan is contained in living things, directing and mastering matter, capable of overcoming many obstacles, perhaps even capable of becoming manifest.

With this in mind, the newness of things is only apparent, since they have long been developing within this immanent dynamism. And we can conclude that, since seminal causes can be found everywhere, inert matter after all hardly differs from living matter, and the passage from matter to life is almost normal. Shall we ever succeed in knowing all the possibilities inherent in matter, all the processes it contains?

"I think"—wrote Claude Bernard—"that an infinite number of living things must exist potentially in nature, and that we do not know them. These living things must be in some way asleep, and waiting. They must appear when the conditions for their existence become actual, and once they have appeared, they must perpetuate themselves, inasmuch as their conditions of life and reproduction also perpetuate themselves."

THE EXPLANATION FROM TRANSCENDENCE

Instead of seeking within the organism for the ultimate cause of its dynamism and its first appearance, let us seek it outside and above it, in a Mind that rules it more or less directly.

We find ourselves here back at the creation—not the

creation of seminal causes, which may have to wait a long time till their moment comes, but the direct creation of the individual. Obviously we must not imagine creation as children do sometimes: God making out of nothing things that instantly arise from the Void in all their splendor, as the divine word is pronounced. Creation has nothing in common with tricks of sleight-of-hand, and has little need of the spectacular trappings with which we often associate it. Let us say at once, in order to clarify the problem, that if by some impossible chance we had been present at the moment when life was first created, at the very moment of God's intervention, we would not have seen an old man with a beard conscientiously kneading matter, or giving it commands, but perhaps merely the sequence of events that a biochemist might imagine, without anything extraordinary interfering with the normal unfolding of the laws of nature. But this unfolding would not by itself have led events down that improbable road which leads to life, and the least error would have wrecked everything; so it was God who directed events in order to bring about the appearance of life. And it is here that we arrive at the theory of St. Thomas Aquinas and his conception of the world and of divine action.

In order to understand it, we must see how his acknowledged master, Aristotle, explained the appearance of life. For Aristotle, as for all the ancients, chemistry reduced everything to four elements, earth, water, air and fire: all the universe was made out of them, and especially living things, where these four elements were found in definite ratios.[7] There is nothing peculiar in thinking that a more or less appropriate mixture should be made out of earth, water and air, especially in mud or in damp places; the only thing necessary for life is fire, the fourth element— not our ordinary fire, which, far from being a vital fire is destructive of life, but the true fire, the true vital warmth, at once soft and pleasant, which comes from the sun or is formed in the fermentation of organic matter. Life, therefore, arose from damp places that had been warmed by the sun or by fermentation.

"All animals that are spontaneously formed," wrote Aristotle, "whether in the earth or in the water, seem to be all born in corruption, to which rainwater is added. It is not that creatures really arise out of corruption, but that they are formed in the act of coction. Corruption, and corrupted matter, are the remains of what has gone through a preliminary coction. The whole of matter is not used in forming these creatures, any more than it is in a work of art: if it were, art could do nothing. As it is, art discards matter that is of no use to it, and so does nature. Animals and plants are born in earth and water, because there is water in the earth, and air in the water, and a vital warmth in every thing, so that we may see life and soul everywhere. Moreover, creatures hasten to develop when this warmth is shut in and enclosed; as the liquids warm up, the heat is concentrated and a sort of bubble of foam produced. The

[7] How things repeat themselves! Nowadays we say that the biosphere, the envelope about the globe in which life is possible, is formed by the lithosphere (the earth), the hydrosphere (water) and the atmosphere (air), to which is added the energy of the sun (fire).

differences that make one kind of animal more advanced, and another more backward, spring from the way in which the vital principle has been enclosed; the phenomenon is caused according to the environment and the substance that is shut in."[8]

Thus, according to Aristotle the appearance of life becomes physically possible when the environment containing the necessary elements lacks only the heat of the sun or the heat of organic corruption.

Faced with this explanation, which everyone regarded as being scientific, Aquinas constructed a whole theory of generation. Normal generation is possible when the female receives the sperm, in which the influence of the male is actualized; the energy of the male does not come from him alone but from the sun as well, in which the influence of the whole environment is made potent. "Man engenders man, but so does the sun," St. Thomas wrote many times, quoting Aristotle. The sun, great font of energy, depends for its power on the angels of God, which rule it; and so we can mount from cause to cause up to God, the essential cause that Malebranche called the only one.

In this hierarchy, which descends from God to the newborn creature, passing through angels, stars, the male and the sperm, everything comes from God, in primal cause; the role of the secondary causes is to define this power more and more precisely. For the generation of the higher animals, the entire series is necessary, while the lower animals can be born without the intervention of the male or the sperm, thanks to the sun, whose action need not

[8] *The Generation of Animals* (Cambridge: Harvard University Press).

be directed very accurately. In this way the spontaneous appearance of life does not astonish the philosopher, who can leave to the scientist the task of finding out how it all actually happened.

For Aristotle, as for Aquinas, life is characterized by the presence of a "psyche," or soul, which, though resembling in many ways the seminal cause, differs from it in that it does not exist before the creature is ready to receive it. Birth is here an event, a beginning, while where seminal causes are in question, it is only an apparition, an unveiling. In matter that is still inert, therefore, there are no germs of life or anything capable of bringing matter to life, but only the chance of providing all the necessary elements for a viable organism: life appears the moment the organism is formed, for God is wise and provident enough not to have to work miracles here and there to influence events that have not developed according to his desires.

Modern thinkers who follow St. Thomas have abandoned the scientific explanations of Aristotle, just as the materialists have abandoned those of Lucretius, for if philosophical positions hardly ever change, we cannot say the same of science, which advances with dizzying speed. The essential point for the Thomist is that life is so absolutely different from matter that he cannot allow the existence of any process by which the one turns into the other: a creature is alive or it is not, and the barrier exists, even if the scientist does not know where to place it.

Strictly speaking, one living creature might be able to provoke the appearance of a lower organism, though science has apparently shown that this does not happen; but it is not denied a priori that man could bring this about with his superior intelligence.

The first living creature appeared in the wastes of the primitive ocean. The Thomist cannot believe that this event, so rich in consequence, could possibly be the result of chance; and since it has occurred despite its improbability, is not this appearance of life a real creation, one of the clearest proofs of the existence and action of God?

Confronting these classic and traditional ways of thought is a wavering and varied "philosophy" whose ideal is to make use of the latest scientific developments. When the problem of "spontaneous generation" was finally settled, another axiom was cautiously advanced: "The transition from matter to life is impossible." From Pasteur's experiments a conclusion was reached by some oversimplifying thinkers, who at once placed it in the company of those philosophical truths that cannot be questioned; and they talked with more or less indulgent condescension about those medieval philosophers who had believed in the possibility of a transition between matter and life. Soon, however, Stanley discovered that filterable viruses could be crystallized, and some scientists wondered if they should still keep matter and life apart. Here, cried our philosophers, is science's last word on the subject; and so, mixing the Thomist and the Augustinian traditions, they set themselves to read through the medieval writers to find what transitions and possibilities of change their masters in opportunism had so carefully effaced. A kind of panpsychism appeared—often more or less disguised—in which

matter could no longer be distinguished from life; for together with living matter there existed another kind of
matter, which does not appear to be alive but which in
reality is virtually alive, which perhaps will come alive,
which only asks to live. . . .

Many philosophical attitudes can be taken toward
biogenesis; we have reduced them to four, two materialist
and two vitalist. Those philosophers who do not want to
acknowledge God will naturally adopt one of the first two,
while those who are not troubled by God's activity will
choose one of the other two. Those who are disconcerted
by discontinuity and sudden change will adopt dialectical
materialism, or perhaps the hidden dynamism of the seminal causes, while others invoke chance or creation in order to
account for the appearance of what is truly an innovation
on our planet: Life.

Scientifically, the field is wide open, and believer and
non-believer search with the same zeal for the process that
heralded the appearance of life. But while the believers
reproach materialists for invoking a gratuitous miracle, or
conjuring the difficulty away by using an indulgent dialectic, materialists accuse believers of looking for too re-
mote a cause, and of invoking God in the creation of life.

5 / The Conditions for Biogenesis

After having looked at the different aspects of the problem raised by the origin of life, we must now try to see how this origin could have taken place, and how we can reach understanding of it.

We can suppose a priori that the origin of life in inert matter was a normal event or that it could only take place in other times and in circumstances that we must describe. The problem is valid for the present time, but it especially concerns first origins.

The Present Time

Pasteur demonstrated by his remarkable experiments that microbes arose, not by biogenesis, but by normal means of reproduction. He did not prove that biogenesis was impossible, and all his experiments are negative, since their only aim was to show that life could not appear. A single positive and well-managed experiment is alone necessary, therefore, to show the possibility that it could. There have been so many and such varied attempts that the conviction has arisen that success is impossible.

These experiments have not been made on infra-microbes, bacteriophages and viruses for the good reason that, at the present stage of science, this is not possible. Pasteur showed that life would not appear in a completely sterilized environment, where life was not already present; how then can such an experiment succeed when dealing with parasites, which cannot live without a living host? If we kill the bacteria, it is plain that the bacteriophages cannot maintain themselves, even if they should be born. How, in any case, shall we be sure that we have killed all the bacteriophages? Or how shall we maintain a culture of bacteria so that they flourish in spite of our precautions against an infection by bacteriophages? The problem is even more difficult for viruses, because of the immense difference in size between parasite and host. We must confess that the problem is beyond us as yet. If in consequence we say that biogenesis does not exist for bacteriophages and viruses—supposing that they are really alive—this is not based on experiments but on an induction from Pasteur's work, an induction that we must say appears quite legitimate and against which there still exists no valid argument.

However, if such a biogenesis occurred nowadays, we would have to say that the main difficulty would be in perceiving it and in proving that no germs had been present in the environment where the new viruses appeared.

Both in the Middle Ages and in the Renaissance it

was admitted that biogenesis and normal reproduction occurred together. Today we cannot see the necessity or even the interest in admitting this abnormal method of generation, when the normal one explains everything.

First Origins

If the problem of biogenesis hardly comes into the picture for life nowadays, this is not so for life at the beginning. How did they first appear on our planet, those first primitive creatures from which possibly all living things are descended?

These answers can be given: life has always existed on our globe; life came from elsewhere; or life has been born on our planet; and it is here that biogenesis enters as a problem.

No theory either affirms or explains that life has always existed on the earth. Some, like Vernadsky—struck by the fact that biogenesis is difficult to imagine—have asked themselves if, after all, life is not eternal, and if to think of its first appearance is not a false problem. Pasteur himself, tired of ceaselessly examining the problem of how life could arise from matter, once asked himself if one could not reverse the question, and look for the origin of matter in life.

If Pasteur and Vernadsky were thinking of a spiritual life, the problem no longer belongs to science but is a philosophical one, such as we have just considered; if they thought about material life, their hypotheses have so little basis as hardly to be worth examining. We know perfectly well that our planet has not always existed, at least not in its present form, and that the most ancient rocks we can date, by means of their radioactive elements—the uranites and monazites of Canada—seem to have been formed between two hundred million and two billion years ago. If we go even further back into time, no one would maintain the permanence of our planet, and there are innumerable theories, from that of Laplace to that of Weizsäcker, that try to explain the various stages of its evolution: in none of these theories can we see how any living things as we know them could possibly exist at such times. For example, if, as Chandrasekhar maintains, the proportion of the elements of our planet shows that it must have long existed at a temperature of 800,000 degrees with a density of ten tons a cubic centimeter, it is impossible to imagine how the faintest trace of life could have remained.

The second answer is somewhat more likely. If life is not contemporaneous with our planet, it could have come from elsewhere: this is the theory of panspermy: the earth was fecundated from across space.

It is possible to think that such germs were brought to us by meteorites, and we think especially of the famous meteorite that fell in 1864 near the village of Orgeuil, France, thirty kilometers north of Toulouse. This meteorite exploded before touching the earth, and its fragments were scattered over an area with a diameter of more than ten kilometers; the fragments contained more than 6 per cent of organic matter, which Berthelot called "carbonaceous"; in 1961 these were investigated by scientists from Fordham University and discovered to be saturated hydrocarbons. Among them, as in living matter, there was a superabundance of the C_{18} and C_{23} forms. There were also identified the traces of five different kinds of microscopic algae (at least a fiftieth of a millimeter in diameter), of which four were related to terrestrial species. The presence of these compounds seems to point to the existence of a planet on which life is well installed, but its localization poses such problems that we must ask if it is not perhaps our own.

Whatever be the case, we must now consider, not whether a meteroite can bear witness to life on other planets, but whether it could bring us the germs of such life. Let us suppose that it comes from an inhabited planet, and bears with it the precious germs. Meteorites come into contact with our atmosphere at such a speed that their surfaces incandesce and melt; any germ lodged on them would thus go through a nasty moment, and would be unlikely to survive. If the germs had got inside the meteorite through small fissures, contact with our atmosphere would produce such a brutal shock that the meteorite would burst and the tiny shelter disappear.

Arrhenius imagines that germs, if electrically charged, could arrive at our planet through the pressure of radiation. Here there are three points to consider: the departure, the voyage and the arrival.

The departure normally would be from a planet on which life flourishes, a planet whose atmospheric layers are no doubt not so different from our own. But Pasteur showed that germs become so rare with increasing altitude that there can hardly be any ten kilometers away from the surface. How, indeed, would they ascend? The pressure of solar radiation cannot carry particles away from the earth's attraction unless their diameter is less than ten millionths of a millimeter, and we have seen that the smallest viruses have a diameter a hundred times larger, and thus a volume a million times as great. Thus the pressure of radiation could not detach them from the earth, and they could only ascend by making use of atmospheric currents; but these currents do not seem to mount very high.

Let us suppose that the departure has been achieved, and even that the germ has not lost its electric charge while passing through the ionosphere, which is a conductor. It goes on its way at a speed that we shall generously suppose to be a hundred times greater than that of artificial satellites, i.e. at a thousand kilometers a second. Let us suppose that it is going directly toward the nearest star, at this dizzy speed; it would need more than a thousand years to arrive, and this time will be much greater the further away the star. Although planets have been discovered around a certain number of stars, it is by no means certain that our nearest neighbor, star Wolf 424, had planets one or two hundred thousand years ago, with all the necessary conditions for life and for germs capable of enduring such an enormous journey. Besides this, these germs would have been for more than a millennium isolated and naked in interstellar space, exposed to an excessively high temperature, and above all, to ultraviolet radiations capable, as Becquerel has shown, of annihilating every living germ in six hours. What then would have happened to them in a thousand years?

Let us be generous and suppose that such germs can leave their environment and remain alive for millennia, despite all the obstacles in their way: they still have to land, and this is not the least dangerous part. For one, the earth cannot exert a pull on them from so far away, and it would thus be pure chance—how improbable a chance!—that the germ took exactly the right direction in order to arrive. Let us allow chance to work for us even here: the speed at which contact with our atmosphere takes place makes it impossible to suppose that the germ is not destroyed, and this forces us to abandon completely this ingenious theory of panspermy and of the fecundation of the world, unless we suppose that it was the work of adventurous astronauts who, some two hundred thousand years ago, touched down on our planet from some distant star!

In any case, this solution is not very satisfying, for it only displaces the problem, by putting it further back. For how did life start in the place from which our astronautic germs set sail? If their planet had been fecundated also, we must go back and back till we come to the original starting place of life. It must have started somewhere, for it is difficult to imagine that it is eternal and that it existed in that primitive atom which Lemaître offers to our imagination when the innumerable galaxies speeding through space had not yet begun their vertiginous expansion.

After having shown that life cannot always have existed on our earth, and that it is pointless to look elsewhere for its origin, only one solution remains, namely that life appeared one fine day on our planet. It seems impossible not to admit a veritable biogenesis here: nothing was alive on our globe and suddenly life arose here and there. How can science explain such a phenomenon?

How Did Life Appear?

The origin of a living creature poses such complex problems that we must ask the questions one by one and divide the difficulty in as many pieces as is necessary to properly resolve it.

We shall attack the problem from four different angles: the thermodynamic, the physical, the organic and the cosmic.

THE THERMODYNAMIC ASPECT

Life is based on complex chemical structures whose most obvious character is to be endothermic and to thus provide a basis on which life's exothermic reactions can be carried out. The first problem is thus to accumulate energy and to build those complex organic structures without which life cannot even start, let alone maintain itself.

Energy can come from various sources, the two main ones being the heat of the earth and that of the sun. As the earth cooled it reached a temperature of several thousand degrees, the temperature at which Berthelot was able to synthesize and condense acetylene, and at which the formation of several substances is possible. These would not yet be complex and unstable, being heterocyclic substances like pyrroles, which are synthesized from two molecules of acetylene and one of ammonia; or like pyridine, synthesized likewise, with hydrocyanic acid instead of ammonia. These substances are of great importance for living things, because the respiratory pigments of plants—chlorophyll—and of animals—hemoglobin—have a porphyrin base, which itself is made of four pyrrole molecules. Later, more unstable substances become possible, and since the atmosphere contains many hydrocarbons such as methane, it is only necessary for oxygen to be joined to these molecules of carbon and hydrogen for glucosides to be formed.

After the earth has cooled, the most important and interesting energy is that which is radiated from the sun. Nowadays little ultraviolet light—which is the most active part of the spectrum—arrives on the earth's surface, being stopped by ozone and oxygen; ozone stops that part next to visible radiations, the wave lengths being between three hundred and two hundred and fifty millionths of a millimeter; oxygen stops wave lengths below that. This nearly total blocking of ultraviolet at the earth's surface makes life possible, for its rays are so active that they would turn the earth into a wilderness if they played freely over it. Observations made with artificial satellites show us that ultraviolet rays penetrate with ease to within fifty kilometers of the earth's surface, but then begin to diminish, and almost disappear at less than twenty-five kilometers.

Before life appeared, the earth's atmosphere did not contain either oxygen or ozone, but was made up of carbon dioxide, nitrogen, rare gases and water vapor: none of these gases stop ultraviolet. On the other hand, ultraviolet can hardly penetrate water, especially sea water, with its bromides and ammonia, and this is why we cannot expect ultraviolet to be very active below a depth of a few centimeters.

Moreover, the formation of organic substances, which we shall speak of in a moment, did not occur on dry land but in the sea, for chemical reactions usually require water. As these organic substances are a little heavier than water and sink slowly to depths at which solar radiation cannot penetrate, the only accumulation of interest to us is that which occurs in very shallow lagoons, whose beds are within reach of ultraviolet light. According to Dauvillier, in this way life is able to make use of active radiations without being destroyed by them.

THE PHYSICAL ASPECT

One of the characteristics of life that Pasteur often stressed was its dissymmetrical structure. This structure, which is due to the carbon atom, whose four valences are saturated by atoms or other elements, is seen above all in its power to rotate light to the right or the left. There are both a dextrose and a laevose glucose, each able to rotate light, but in opposite directions. If we synthesize glucose, we shall obtain as much dextrose as laevose, a mixture called *racemic glucose*, in which the rotation of light is canceled through exact compensation.

Now dextrose alone is found in all plants and animals, and if we make mold cultures on racemic glucose, we find them using only the dextrose and leaving the laevose. When faced by the variety of asymmetrical organic substances, life always makes the same choice.

Pasteur once worked on this problem: he tried to make a glucose that was not racemic but only dextrose or only laevose, by introducing factors causing dissymmetry at the moment crystallization took place. Work on the same lines by many other scientists has achieved a minimal success by using polarized light. Must we conclude that in certain conditions at the beginning light was thus polarized?

But instead of looking for a cosmic cause for this dissymmetry, can we not think of a chance event, for instance, a quartz crystal polarizing the light that made the first dissymmetrical molecule appear? In the slowly forming world, this molecule would have played the role of a catalyst in bringing all succeeding syntheses in line with its own structure. Chance would thus have caused the direction in which the dissymmetry occurred, if not the dissymmetry itself.

THE ORGANIC ASPECT

An abundance of organic and dissymmetrical matter has carpeted the beds of Pre-Cambrian lagoons, but life has not yet appeared. It is a critical and decisive moment.

Have you ever witnessed the following surprising phenomenon on a cold morning in early winter? A pond has slowly cooled during the frosty night and the temperature of its surface has even descended below freezing point. There is as yet no ice, but the moment a minute crystal forms, wherever it may be, a sheet of ice spreads out and in a few minutes has covered the entire pond. Everything was ready: only the germ was needed.

The fact of crystallization is still quite mysterious. Ice forms in water without much difficulty, but glycerine, though it normally melts at a temperature of 18° C., was seen to crystallize for the first time during the winter of 1867, in some barrels that were being sent from Vienna to London. Since then glycerine crystals have been easily obtained by using a seed from a previous batch of crystals. The appearance of life is a much more difficult problem than this first crystallization of glycerine, and presupposes a number of stages, which we can reduce to three: the formation of ordinary organic molecules; the formation of complex organic molecules such as nucleoproteins that could function as catalysts; and the formation of living entities.

The Appearance of Organic Molecules. In 1910 Berthelot showed that ultraviolet radiation is strong enough to form a good number of organic compounds. Carbon dioxide in water can combine with a molecule of water to form formaldehyde plus an oxygen molecule. Formaldehyde is easily polymerized and by successive aldolizations forms glucose, which in turn can be polymerized to starch, cellulose and so forth.

$$CO_2 + H_2O \rightarrow HCHO + O_2$$
$$6\,HCHO \rightarrow C_6H_{12}O_6$$
$$nC_6H_{21}O_6 \rightarrow (C_6H_{10}O_5)n + nH_2O$$

These results were confirmed by Calvin in 1956, using a cyclotron instead of ultraviolet light; he obtained formic acid, succinic acid and so forth.

While glucosides can be formed in this way, it is possible for carbon dioxide to combine with ammonia rather than water and thus form formic acid. Here we are at the beginning of proteins and all albuminous compounds, for we need only add one molecule of formic amide to one of formaldehyde to obtain an amino acid, glycocoll.

$$CO_2 + NH_3 \rightarrow NH_2COH + O$$
$$NH_2COH + HCHO \rightarrow NH_2CH_2COOH$$

The earth's first atmosphere abounded in methane, ammonia and water, according to Oparin, who claims that these compounds are easily transformed by simple oxidation into the main organic substance; in such an atmosphere Miller has formed amino acids—notably glycocoll and alanine—by electrical discharges. In this way glucosides and proteins, the fundamental substances of living organisms, could have been formed.

The Appearance of Complex Molecules. When plunged into a humid atmosphere or an aqueous solution, hydrocarbons or compounds of light molecular weight tend to undergo extensive polymerization, and complex substances can form if the various metals of the lithosphere are present.

Sagan has pointed out the abundance of phosphorus, so important in the intermediate stages of metabolism. Molecules of ATP (adenyl triphosphate) would be built up, capable of storing energy, and protein molecules capable of using this energy would form. We need only refer to the formation of nucleoproteins of the ADN type (desoxyribonucleic acid) from these proteid and ATPs, thanks to the diastases discovered by Kornberg and Ochoa, and we come to a molecule capable of reproducing itself—to the first virus!

The Formation of Living Entities. While solutions of compounds of light molecular weight are very stable, proteins of heavier molecular weight give rise to colloids that are relatively unstable and often coagulate into coacervates.

Devaux has shown that a certain number of organic molecules have a double pole, one hydrophile, the other hydrophobe. When lying on a water surface, they eventually form a membrane with very special properties: the hydrophilic poles are directed toward the water, the hydrophobic poles away from it. Such a membrane can only be wetted on its lower surface; water will not stick on its upper surface. This curious opposition nicely demonstrates the difference between the inner and outer surfaces of living membranes. Living membranes cannot be wetted from the outside. While water accumulates inside the membrane, where it forms a large proportion of the cytoplasm, the exterior secretes waxes. If such a membrane formed around our nucleoprotein molecules, we would not have far to go before we arrived at simple organisms like bacteria and cyanophytes. Inside this membrane the processes of life can take place, and the organism slowly develops and becomes individualized.

Although they are heterotrophic—that is, incapable of finding nourishment by themselves—bacteria could have been the first living things, according to our hypothesis, since organic matter was plentiful.

The first major development was the appearance of chlorophyll among the cyanophytes. This pigment allows the plant to be autotrophic, to stop being dependent on already formed organic matter, and to start on its evolutionary conquest of the world with its own resources.

Another essential development was that of the nu-

cleus of the cell. We may suppose that the protein molecules that were the first sketch of the chromosomes came
together and were surrounded by a membrane at the center
of the cell, which was thus fully formed.

So, helped by a fate that we can only call benevolent,
all the syntheses and transformations were accomplished
thanks to which life was born on our globe.

THE COSMIC ASPECT

In order to complete our survey, we must consider
what the conditions on our planet were like for life to appear on it, and what repercussions this event produced.

For life to exist on a planet, a number of conditions
are necessary, above all the presence of water, of an atmosphere, and of the requisite temperature.

The outlying planets—Pluto, Uranus, Neptune, Saturn,
Jupiter and even Mars—cannot support life, because of
their distance from the sun. Jupiter's temperature is $-140°$,
while that of Mars rarely rises higher than $0°$ even in summer on the equator. Water cannot exist except as ice on the
surface of Jupiter. The atmosphere consists of methane and
ammonia. Life cannot be possible. Life is improbable on
Mars also, unless in a very rudimentary form, for its atmosphere is very rare—a pressure of only a few centimeters of
mercury—and composed above all of carbon dioxide. Moreover, a nearly absolute drought reigns over the entire
planet. Life is impossible on both Mercury and the Moon,
for their mass is too small for them to have retained an
atmosphere. There remains Venus, about which we know
very little because of its permanent cloudiness. Some of the

conditions that make life possible seem to be found there, but the period of its rotation, which is about a month, would make the water of its surface freeze at night and boil during the day: it is hard for life to adapt itself to such excessive conditions, and it is much more probable that it does not exist there.

Earth would thus be the only place in our solar system where life flourishes; if it has appeared by chance on other planets, it has not maintained itself there. Does it exist also outside our solar system, on a planet of some star in our galaxy, or else in one of the innumerable galaxies hurtling through space? It is as hard to affirm this as to deny it, and we are reduced to the idlest speculations on the existence and evolution of life on these rival planets.

Let us return to Earth, whose atmosphere and soil will be profoundly changed by life. Plants synthesize organic matter through the action of chlorophyll by using carbon dioxide and releasing oxygen, which is found first in the water and then in the atmosphere where it becomes increasingly abundant. Much of it is turned into ozone by the action of ultraviolet light, and this ozone comes to intercept more and more of the ultraviolet, whose harmful qualities no doubt forced the first living things to shelter under enough water to minimize the effects. Soon, sheltered by the growing layer of ozone, living things could come to the surface of the water without risk, and much later come onto dry land. Let us not forget that this protective screen has grown to exactly the right dimensions; for if it grew larger the feeble ultraviolet radiation that still arrives from the sun and that allows organisms to turn ergosterol into vitamin D would be entirely cut off, and rickets would permanently establish itself over the world.

Life modifies not only the atmosphere but the lithosphere as well. All the rocks that have been slowly deposited and formed since life appeared on the earth are more or less impregnated with its traces. The enormous layers of chalk are formed from the remains of skeletons and shells of organisms, some of which were immense, while others, the coccoliths, measure some thousandths of a millimeter in diameter. And we need only point at the deposits of coal and oil, formed by the immense piling up of dead organisms that ages ago fermented in fresh or salt water.

Today arable land and humus are largely produced by life. Roots dig into the earth and extract certain compounds after having disintegrated it. A layer of humus usually forms at the surface, and multitudes of bacteria—whose weight has been estimated at half a ton per hectare—colonize this soil. Life makes its mark on the surface of our globe.

The Difficulties

This presentation shows how the various theories about the origins of life can best be put together. Though the story appears solid and coherent, many matters are still unexplained, and we must now look at some of the difficulties that spring to mind in considering these theories.

We must first say that the theories make considerable play with chance: they have this right, since they are not taking up a philosophical position. They want to show us *how* things could have happened, but they do not even ask why. Berthelot, for example, synthesized organic matter with the aid of ultraviolet rays, under very precise conditions. Obviously such an event is not impossible, if a chemist can bring it about, but laboratory conditions are strictly defined, and if some enormous variations may not hinder the experiment being carried out successfully, other, minimal ones may.

Do we have the right to presuppose that essential conditions shall come into existence by chance, that the proportion of elements will be just right, together with the temperature and radiation? Can we believe that conditions will be maintained for synthesis to be carried out, but not for hydrolysis? When no organic molecule existed, ultraviolet radiation of course could not destroy it; but once such molecules came into being, how come this radiation—more famous for its destructive than its constructive activity—did not destroy them even before they had time to sink below the protective layer of water? Can evolution, with its one-way direction toward synthesis, be explained by chance?

Let us remain on scientific ground. One difficulty seems to be the initial absence of oxygen. Before the appearance of life, the atmosphere had no free oxygen in it, any more than the sea had, since the only reaction capable of producing it was that provoked by chlorophyll, which had not yet been formed. The synthesis of glucosides by ultraviolet light must have freed some oxygen, but Dauvillier thinks it must have been very little and that "the first geochemical result of the presence of chlorophyll was the creation of an abundant atmosphere of free oxygen."

Free oxygen is produced by the action of chlorophyll, but it seems to have been forgotten that plants breathe, and require quite a large quantity of free oxygen for respiration. When the pressure of oxygen is reduced, plants have recourse to a reaction that yields little and produces poisons: glucose, or fructose, is separated into alcohol and carbon dioxide, in the following reaction

$$C_6H_{12}O_6 \rightarrow 2\ C_2H_5OH + 2\ CO_2$$

This anaerobic respiration cannot go on long, because the cells are soon killed by the alcohol thus produced.

In full sunlight, we can just about admit, a plant well provided with chlorophyll can manage to live in an environment without oxygen, as long as it can retain the oxygen it produces. Can it? Oxygen is hardly soluble in water and frees itself immediately; it must be very abundant in the atmosphere before an appreciable quantity can remain in the water. The outlook is equally depressing for plants, which can only produce oxygen after their development; and this period is the most active and demanding of their lives.

As for photosynthesis, we must ask ourselves if conditions were ideal for it. Nowadays it takes place with 0.03 per cent of carbon dioxide in the atmosphere. If we increase the quantity of this gas, the reaction will become proportionately more active until we reach about 10 per cent, but for stronger concentrations, the reaction diminishes, stopping almost entirely at 50 per cent: carbon dioxide becomes paralyzing at high doses.

But was carbon dioxide at such a level? It does not

seem so a priori, for the equilibrium it forms with bi-carbonates and carbonates, especially in the oceans, has always allowed it to maintain its pressure at something like the level it is at today. In such conditions paralysis need not be feared; but can we invoke an abundance of carbon dioxide for the first organic syntheses?

If the small amount of oxygen poses a problem for us at the beginning, its excessive quantity in the atmosphere today is equally disconcerting. Its mass appears to be constant, somewhere between one and two quadrillion tons.

All this oxygen comes from plants, but let us not forget that the disoxygenated carbon of plants and animals is capable of taking back all the oxygen that photosynthesis has freed from it; and that all the actions of living things, every oxygen reduction, quickly approaches this state of total reoxidation, and inevitably recaptures the oxygen photosynthesis has freed. It follows that the only free oxygen either in the air or in the water corresponds to the carbon of living matter. Vernadsky estimates the weight of every living organism at the order of a quadrillion tons, but Cailleux claims it is fifty times less abundant, twenty trillion tons at most. In order to favor our theory as much as we can, let us take a figure between the two, say a hundred trillion tons, ten times less than the minimum amount of free oxygen in the atmosphere. Carbon represents some 12 or 18 per cent of this living matter, i.e. about a seventh (fourteen trillion tons). If completely disoxygenated, this carbon would correspond to about thirty-seven trillion tons of oxygen, since three grams of carbon will fix eight of oxygen. Even supposing that this amount is not overestimated—

since the carbon in living organisms is already more or less oxygenated—we have only accounted for a thirtieth of the total of free oxygen: and if life disappeared entirely, taking with it all the oxygen it has liberated, 97 per cent of the oxygen in the atmosphere would still remain.

In addition to living matter, there are, fortunately, large stocks of once-living matter that are as yet unoxidized, namely coal and oil. We reoxidize them when we burn them, but as long as they are not burned, they are a store of disoxygenated carbon; since they represent the only remaining reserves, they must correspond to the mass of free oxygen that their disoxygenation freed, and that remains free as long as they are not reoxidized.

But the world reserves of coal are estimated at about ten trillion tons, and those of oil at a thousand times smaller. We are still a long way from accounting for all the oxygen in the atmosphere—95 per cent of which remains unexplained—unless we reverse the problem (that is, if we are sure that photosynthesis is the only way free oxygen can be liberated, and I do not see why not), and say that the reserves of coal and oil must be a hundred times larger than our estimates.

Even if it is true that the chlorophyll reaction is the only way to produce free oxygen, we must not forget that respiration is by no means the only way oxygen can be fixed: certain metals become oxidized, volcanoes fix oxygen and so do shooting stars, of which twenty-four million enter our atmosphere every day. Disoxygenated carbon and, as a result, living matter should thus be fifty times as abundant as they really are.

Whatever the truth of the matter, this oxygen exists, and we should be happy that it does. It is conceivable that photosynthesis nowadays compensates for the current losses, and that, despite what is used by the respiration of every living thing, despite the combustion taking place in our fireplaces and factories, the balance is more or less maintained. But that life itself could have made such an enormous mass as a reserve must make one thoughtful; and remember that, according to Cailleux, oxygen could also come from the reduction of nitrates by nitrogen-fixing bacteria, which are perhaps the creators of the nitrogen in the atmosphere.

Let us also not forget another theory, which radically changes the aspect of the problem. Harteck and Jensen (1948) believe that ultraviolet radiation would dissociate atmospheric water $H_2O \rightarrow H + OH$. While hydrogen is light enough to be carried away and lost to our planet, oxygen would increasingly abound. We must then explain, not why there is so much of it, but why there is so little.

Let us finally note two objections to our theory. It makes formaldehyde the intermediary in the synthesis of glucosides 5, which is troublesome. Formalin is very soluble in water, so much so that the water in which the first living things are to appear will be full of formalin though practically lacking in oxygen. The least we can say is that we would wish a more welcoming environment for the first bacteria.

For Dauvillier, bacteria would in fact be the first living things to appear in the mass of organic matter produced by ultraviolet light. But this does not simplify the problem:

bacteria take all their energy from oxidation, and if they can do without free oxygen in their anaerobic phase, this does not mean that their energy is not diminished, or that a sizable amount of carbon is turned into carbon dioxide. It is thus better for the theory to admit that bacteria were not the first comers, destroying the precious capital of organic matter in an instant, but that plants with chlorophyll were the first to profit by it.

We must therefore conclude that life could hardly have become installed on our planet without photosynthesis, while with chlorophyll it can launch out and shift for itself.

6 / In Search of the First Living Things

Through his study of even the smallest piece of evidence, the paleontologist manages to reconstruct, more or less adequately, "images of vanished worlds."[1] He peoples them only with organisms he is sure of, whose appearance and way of life he has tried to determine from their skeletons. He knows very well that there must have been many more fragile organisms, which left no remains but which occupied an important place in their own world. In whatever field he works, and as soon as he goes even a short distance into the past, the historian is quite conscious that side by side with perfectly precise facts there are many others that he is quite ignorant of, and that these may even form the greater part of the picture he is trying painfully to reconstruct. We are not independent of Time, but profoundly engaged in a story irreversible in its advance, which makes it nearly as hard to see backward as to see the

[1] Quoted from M. Piveteau, professor of paleontology at the Sorbonne, and the principal authority for this chapter.

future. Imprisoned in our time, it is difficult to reanimate vanished epochs.

Toward Our Origins

However, let us trust ourselves to the paleontologists and go back into the past toward the first origins of life. Here we do not count in thousands of years, but in millions and almost in billions.

If we could go back a million years, we would see no apparent change in nature or in the landscape, with the same plants and trees we are accustomed to, the same animals and birds. The one thing that would astonish us is that there would be no trace of man, not one of those traces that today cover everything: man is one of the last arrivals in the kingdom of life.

If we go back a hundred million years, the scene would still be more or less the same. A specialist, however, would note many differences, for in the Secondary, in the middle of the Cretaceous, we would be overwhelmed by the abundance of reptiles.

Let us go back further: four hundred million years, to the middle of the Silurian. This time the change is remarkable. The continents are a bare and empty desert; life floats in the waters, strange in appearance and in the absence of many well-known forms, though it is nonetheless varied and abundant. There are no fish or vertebrates, but invertebrates crowd among the algae (certain of which are known to us today, since they have crossed the intervening millennia without much change). No stalk yet emerges from the water, and we must wait fifty million years before Psilophyton dares to do so, to become one of the ancestors of our terrestrial flora. At much the same epoch the first vetebrate appears, an equally fateful ancestor.

Geological Eras	Dates (in millions of years)	Plants	Animals
Quaternary	–		Man
Tertiary			
Secondary ⎰ Cretaceous – ⎱ Jurassic ⎰ Triassic	100 –		Birds
		Angiosperms	Mammals
	– 200 –		Reptiles
Primary ⎰ Permian ⎱ Carboniferous ⎰ Devonian ⎰ Silurian ⎱ Cambrian	300 –	Gymnosperms	Amphibians
	400 –	Vascular cryptograms	Fish
	500 –		
	– 600 –		
Pre-Cambrian	700 –		
	800 –		
	900 –		
	1000 –		Inverte-
	1100 –	Bacteria and	brates (?)
	1200 –	Blue	
	1300 –	algae (?)	
	1400 –		
	1500 –		
	–		

NOTE: The principal dates in evolution are: Pre-Cambrian (more than a thousand million years); Primary (400 millions), 5 periods, 17 stages; Secondary (150 million), 3 periods, 24 stages; Tertiary (50 million), 4 periods, 17 stages; and Quaternary (600,000 years).

The main groups in the animal and vegetable kingdoms are named opposite the approximate date at which they appeared.

Paleontology allows us to go back another hundred million years, but stops short at the beginning of the Cambrian, the dawn of primeval time. Are we then at the beginning of life? What fauna and flora do we see at this moment, five hundred million years distant from us? Let us say first of all that nothing seems to have changed during these hundred million years: life has not made any startling innovations, and besides, the evidence becomes increasingly rare as we go further back into the past. However, thanks to the famous schist beds at Burgess in British Columbia, we can again make an inventory of the various living forms; but it is the last we shall be able to establish unless some sensational and unexpected discovery again pushes back the horizon. Plants are represented by numerous and varied algae, but nothing else, except for microsopic bacteria. Animals are much more varied, and most of the marine invertebrates are there: foraminifers, sponges, medusae, echinoderms, worms, lamellibranchs and gastropods. We are thus still very far from the origins of life. We must go further back; but can we?

It is useful to recall the main difficulties encountered in going back into the past; this will at least make us appreciate at its proper value the meager evidence the paleontologists work so hard to uncover.

Thanks to the variety of fossils that have been found, paleontologists can subdivide geological formations into stages. They can subdivide them the better the more fossils there are and the better known the period. In the Cambrian, which lasted a longer time than the whole Tertiary but is represented by an equal thickness of deposits, only three stages have been established, while the Tertiary has seventeen, the most distant ones fading into the mist.

Let us not forget that each stage's position is defined by the stages above and below it. Here there is no lower stage, and the fossils found before the Cambrian are much too rare to let us make any distinctions in a formation as thick as all the ones above together. The lowest layer need not necessarily be Pre-Cambrian. Even if there seems to be a layer below the lowest Cambrian stage—the Georgian—it is difficult to define at all exactly what belongs to the Pre-Cambrian. The problem is even more complicated when, for instance, a Silurian level lies out of sequence on more ancient levels; and we often wonder whether these formations can or should be subjoined to the Pre-Cambrian.

Another even more annoying point is the disappearance of fossils, destroyed in metamorphic rocks. Often deep-lying sedimentary levels are transformed into crystalline rock, either by means of granitic intrusions or by *fumeroles*. Such a transformation, although it often respects the stratification of the rock, profoundly alters its intimate structure: fossils disappear in this crystallization and general reorganization. The most deep-lying formations are obviously the first affected by metamorphism, and suffer the gravest changes. With justice we can say that the earth, by metamorphism, has burned its oldest archives. This loss is irreparable.

It is certain, therefore, that many organisms, although originally fossilized, are unknown to us, for even in the center of the rocks occasions for destruction have not been lacking, in a billion years. However, thick layers of Pre-

Cambrian formations exist here and there, above all in America, and paleontologists have been surprised to find very little traces of life in them, even where the rock is not metamorphic. How explain this surprising rarity? Many theories have been proposed.

The geologist Chamberlin suggested that organisms did not become fossilized at that time because they lived on dry land and not in the water, which they only entered in the Cambrian. As fossilization is difficult when not in water, we have no fossils of these first organisms. This solution, made to measure, lacks not only proofs but likelihood.

A better and more likely explanation is that organisms fossilize better if their skeletons have calcium in them, and that the first organisms had no calcium. This absence can be explained either physiologically or chemically.

We are in an epoch when the only animals are invertebrates. There are few remains in which calcium is abundant, except for shells, those of lamellibranchs, for example. But these creatures move with difficulty and live most of their lives fixed to the bottom: their protection is so good that they have lost the need to move. This protection must have been a secondary adaptation, and only appeared in the Cambrian. During the Pre-Cambrian, life floated as plankton on the surface of the oceans. Animals maneuvered near the surface, in order to find their food; agility was much more important to them than protection.

This answer to the problem is quite attractive, for a number of reasons.

"The composition of the Cambrian fauna," says Piveteau, "gives some verification of the theory. There were sedentary and free-swimming organisms. The sedentary organisms all secreted a skeleton; sponges had a siliceous skeleton (it was only later that there appeared sponges with a calcareous skeleton); archaeocyathins secreted a calcareous skeleton; cystids were enclosed in a calcareous test. Free-swimming organisms had very nearly no skeleton, for instance, medusae and worms. However, some sedentary tubiculous annelids began to construct calcareous tubes. The burrowing branchiopods had a chitinous shell, lightly impregnated with lime. Many gastropods and cephalopods had a thin calcareous shell. Arthropods had a coat of chitin."

Undoubtedly there is a relationship between being sedentary and having a calcareous skeleton capable of being fossilized. Besides, looking over all the Cambrian fossils, it seems that the sessile habit was not widespread, and this provides another argument in support of the theory. However, we are here dealing with probabilities, not proofs, and we cannot say that the sudden appearance of the sessile habit at the beginning of the Cambrian explains the fact just because it coincides with it.

Does chemistry offer a better explanation of the link between the rarity of calcium and that of fossils?

Some scientists, like Lane, think that the Pre-Cambrian oceans were acid, which would have made it impossible for organisms to build calcareous skeletons, since calcium cannot be fixed in such conditions. It is a fact that calcium plays no part in the shells of these oldest organisms, which are made of chitin or silica: chitin being an organic material, and silica an acid anhydride, their deposition would not be affected by an acid environment.

But were the primeval oceans acid? Why can we not simply posit that the first living organisms had not yet discovered the use of calcium in making a skeleton? This would explain the facts perfectly well, though the theory could not be maintained without proof, since it assumes that life behaved differently from the way it does now. In fact, if organisms did not then use calcium, this was because they did not have it, rather than because they disdained it.

And so we arrive at Daly's theory: The Pre-Cambrian seas lacked calcium. Today the calcium that rivers bring to the sea in the shape of carbonates or bicarbonates is mostly in an ionized state. The numerous marine organisms, which constantly require calcium, soon make inroads into this supply. The formation of carbonate of lime seems to be strictly connected with life, and in uninhabited sea water calcium is precipitated, not as a carbonate, but as a sulfate. Calcium-using animals such as oysters absorb what is in suspension, and not what has already sunk to the bottom. Bischof has calculated that an oyster must pass about fifty thousand times its weight of sea water through its gills, in order to make its shell. At such a rate, it would never have finished it in the Pre-Cambrian seas. The reason for this, which Daly gives, is that there were then no carrion-eaters. Sunk to the bottom, dead bodies would ferment under the action of bacteria and produce quantities of ammonia, which carbon dioxide would transform into ammonium carbonate; when in contact with the sulfate of lime in sea water, this precipitates carbonate of lime as a mud, which animals find it hard to make use of.

For the sea to be well stocked in usable calcium, it has to be well peopled, and dead bodies must not decompose on the ocean floor; this latter condition obviously was lacking.

Seeing that there was a shortage of calcium, it is not strange that organisms did not develop calcareous skeletons. Everyone knows, for instance, that snails are found on chalky ground and are rare elsewhere, because the plants on which they feed are short in this element, and as a result their shells are too weak. In calcium-rich rivers molluscs are more numerous and their shells thicker than in calcium-poor rivers.

However, says L. Cayeux, is it true that the Pre-Cambrian seas were poor in calcium? Is there not a large chalky formation from this epoch in the neighborhood of the St. Lawrence? But the presence of calcium, as we have said, presupposes the existence of organisms that have fixed it in this form; so that there, at least, organisms had calcium at their disposal. The remains of algae of this period also show good use of calcium: it was therefore not unobtainable. Even dolomites were then formed, which means an abundance of lime; but these dolomites are rather strange, and not too much stress should be put on them in this argument.

Whatever the explanation, the fact is there: Pre-Cambrian fossils are not numerous, indeed are much rarer than we have reason to hope. None of the explanations for this state of affairs are perfect, but perhaps each represents part of the truth. We can admit that the sessile habit and necrophagy were much less widespread than today, and that perhaps, in spite of some exceptions here and there, calcium was rather rare in Pre-Cambrian seas.

The First Fossils

Nearly a hundred years ago MacCulloch pointed out some curious structures in the Algonkian gneiss of Canada: alternate bands of calcite and serpentine forming bizarre plaques. Dawson imagined that these were the remains of the very first living organisms, and he called this proto-animal *Eozoon canadense.* Carpenter believed he could identify it, too, and Eozoon became an important fossil in the shape of a giant foraminifer. It was found in Pre-Cambrian formations in Finland, the Pyrenees and so forth. Although some people thought its structure too regular to be that of a living organism, it would all the same have kept a good enough paleontological reputation, if it had not been found at last in the zone of contact in metamorphic rocks. This was the *coup de grâce;* and it lost its last defenders when it was found in calcareous blocks thrown up by Vesuvius.

A certain number of other Pre-Cambrian fossils have followed Eozoon into the outer darkness of lost illusions. It is easy to make mistakes when one is looking for the merest traces of life, and hoping to find them in simple if unexpected forms: certain nodules and structures of rock often seem to be regular enough to be the remains of a living organism. Nonetheless enough undisputed if not indisputable fossils remain for us to take a glimpse at the flora and fauna that peopled the Pre-Cambrian oceans.

The Fauna

We can only form a fragmentary picture of the fauna, and we are not at all sure that some of our fossils will not one day join Eozoon.

Many animals existed of which we will never know anything; many others will be found sooner or later. But the rare fossils that we now possess represent many of the invertebrate branches: radiolarians, coelenterates, foraminifers, sponges, crustacea, crinoids and brachiopods. This list speaks volumes for the progress life made before the beginning of the Primary.

One of the most incontestable of these fossils is Lingullella, with its chitinous test, the representative of that group of brachiopods that was so important in Primary times and that, strangely enough, still exists in much the same form in the Moluccas. It has not evolved for a billion years.

In 1924 Metzger found in the Finnish Pre-Cambrian fossils that seemed to be polyps; he gave them the name *Carelozoon.*

Many other Pre-Cambrian fossils have been discovered all over the world, and if some cannot withstand criticism, quite a few others can. These interesting remains give us some idea of the life of those primeval seas, an idea admittedly very poor and imprecise, for we can hardly imagine that there were no other organisms than those whose fossils we have found. We have every right to believe that this fauna was very rich, for we have indisputable proof of the abundance of living things and their great quantity in the traces of phosphoric acids found in the rocks.

Phosphorus is not rare in the earth's crust, of which it represents about a thousandth part, and is found either as apatite in certain volcanic rocks or much more frequently in the form of small grains or nodules of phosphate of lime. The origin and mode of formation of these nodules is not well understood, but there is no doubt that they came from the decomposition of plant and above all of animal matter; phosphorus makes up about 1 per cent of animal tissue. With changes of sea level, a sea will sometimes dry out or a lake be flooded by sea water; most of the organisms present die and form an immense charnel heap. Decomposition sets in, ammonia is formed and probably saturates the phosphoric acid present in the tissues. Sooner or later this ammonium phosphate will come into contact with carbonate of lime, itself a product of decomposition, and form small concretions of phosphate of lime. Morocco is famous for its phosphates, for they are abundant enough to be exploited: but they date only to the end of the Secondary and the beginning of the Tertiary. Pre-Cambrian phosphates are less abundant, but their existence is indisputable, and bears witness to those ancient charnel heaps; perhaps it offers the only trace we shall ever find of organisms that could not be fossilized because they lacked a skeleton.

Where the charnel heaps decomposed in sea water, they gave rise to oil. Oil has not yet been found in these formations; it would be suprising if it had been, given its volatility, and the occurrence of metamorphism and other geological changes; but its equivalent has been found—in the form of traces of hydrocarbons—in some Pre-Cambrian schists. This also testifies to the abundance of life in those days.

The Flora

We know as little about the flora of this epoch as we do of the fauna. As far as we can judge from the fossils, the flora was more primitive and less varied than the fauna; but then we only have remains of algae and bacteria.

Botanically speaking, the structure of these algae is so imprecise that a new grouping has been made for them apart from extant species, a grouping that is only provisional, and that no doubt they will leave once their structure is sufficiently clear. For the moment they are called *stromatoliths*. The name can hardly compromise them, for it just means "medley of stones," and it says little about their structure.

In 1883 Hall found in the Pre-Cambrian of New York State numerous concretions in concentric and well-zoned beds, which resembled Eozoon in many points, and which he called *Cryptozoon* (the enigmatic animal), thinking it belonged to the animal kingdom. These concretions, which sometimes form veritable reefs, have occasionally been found in the Cretaceous, the Pontien, the Quaternary and especially in Pre-Cambrian formations in Ontario, Greenland and the Gobi Desert.

In 1914 Walcott announced the discovery of a whole series of similar concretions in the Algonkian formation of the Far West, and gave them various names. *Collenia,* with its bossed and more or less concentric ribbon structure, seems to be the remains of organisms that lived near the surface in shallow water: it is found also in China, and in the lower Silurian of Siberia. *Camasia* is flattened and spongy. *Greysonia* is tabular. *Newlandia* is more or less spherical, and comes in successive layers joined here and there by pierced partitions. The oddest of all is *Gallatinia,* with its disklike shape more than ten centimeters across, and with a cross-section like a wheel with seven spokes.

When Eozoon was banished from among the number of the living, an effort was made to send these stromatoliths along with it, by using purely physico-chemical explanations—above all, Liesegang's rings, which are seen in certain diffusions and which can be used to explain some structures found in rock. But the stromatoliths have resisted this attack, and have well fortified their first position.

Walcott, their principal discoverer, sees in them not the remains of plants but the traces of their activity, and he invokes the "biscuits" from Australia: calcareous concretions of varied structure found on the surface, which are non-cellular and remind us somewhat of Cryptozoon. They are produced by blue algae. As we shall see, there is no doubt that these minute algae existed in the Pre-Cambrian, and the stromatoliths present traces of their activity.

Cayeux thinks otherwise, that they are truly the remains of much larger algae, as well developed as a large thallus: the stromatoliths would be the fragments of more or less preserved thalli. He lays stress on the fact that the calcareous concretions produced by blue algae do not show a well-defined structure but are just vaguely concentric. These other algae would be marine, and why should we be surprised to find the numerous and well-developed Pre-Cambrian fauna living on a flora that might be backward but certainly included the thallophytes?

Minute blue algae seem to have been fairly abundant, and they are no doubt the cause of certain calcareous concretions very similar to those produced even now in Lake Michigan. For over a billion years blue algae have lived out their simple and monotonous lives, on the very spot where their ancestors once flourished; nothing has changed for them.

Finland gives us traces of carbon that date back to eleven hundred and fifty million years ago: they are genuine but unrecognizable plant remains, no doubt of some ancient algae, which has been named *Corycium enigmaticum*.

If we admit that the ratio of carbon 12 to carbon 13 next to 91 demonstrates life, life would go back over two and a half billion years, to the stromatoliths of Rhodesia.

In any case, we must not forget bacteria, not because it is logical to suppose they were present, but because we can prove it. At first sight this is surprising: how can microscopic organisms a millionth of a millimeter in size have left lasting traces when other, much larger ones have left nothing!

Their importance has been shown by Renault, and above all by Cayeux, in the formation of minerals: in large measure it is to them that we owe the existence of coal and oil, of phosphates and limes, and of numerous oölitic irons.

These bacteria have been photographed with infrared light with such definition that they can often be identified for genus and even species.

The activity of bacteria is particularly noticeable in ferrous oölites, whose mineralogical composition they slowly change. In various places all the stages of this change can be traced, as if the slow process had been arrested at different times, as it must have been by a change of environment. These bacteria are plentiful in the Huron iron ores of Minnesota, in the Pre-Cambrian soil of Calvados, in the schists of Montana, and so forth.

Sulphur isotopes give us other indications. The variations in their proportions and the increase of the light sulphurs in the course of geological time have led Thode, Macnamara and Fleming (1953) to conclude that sulphur bacteria have existed for 800 million years.

The bacterial flora of the Pre-Cambrian will soon be the best known, thanks to advances in chemistry and microscopy.

The First Living Things

At the end of our inquiry into the latest paleontological studies, we must confess that our curiosity is far from satisfied. We can see that our knowledge of Pre-Cambrian forms is altogether fragmentary: new discoveries, always possible, may yet astonish us and radically alter the image we have of these ancient times. If only we could accurately date the miserable remains we do have! But this period, longer than all the rest put together, is not subdivided in any way, and we cannot tell whether a fossil dates from six hundred million or a billion two hundred million years ago. In such a state of affairs, can we say that one fossil is older than another? This is a difficult problem if the fossils have been found in the sediments of the same region, but it becomes insoluble if one fossil comes from Europe and the other from North America. We can say that they are anterior to the Cambrian, but it is hazardous to say more.

After half a billion years of life, animals had become fairly varied and quite complex in organization, and lived off a primitive flora.

Plant life seems to have waited till the Devonian, when it emerged from the water, to launch into evolutionary progress: well adapted to the marine environment, it had no reason to change till then.

The animals, while they were also entirely marine, showed more dynamism: less satisfied, less well adapted, they also had a less extensive supply of food than plants, which could grow wherever there was sunlight. The less well adapted animals died off, while new mutations led to notable and varied progress.

One fact is nevertheless well established: the first living things were simple organisms. We can even extrapolate back down the evolutionary line to a time of which we have as yet no knowledge at all, and say that these primeval beings were very simple. During a half billion years of geological time, we can see them becoming more and more complex: so we can legitimately assume that the same development was taking place in the previous half billion years.

What were these first living beings? Obviously they

were not animals—what would they have eaten?—but plants. The best bet would be the blue algae, the simplest in structure and yet quite capable of getting along on their own. They are indeed found among the earliest forms, and it is hard to deny their antiquity. Only bacteria can dispute first place with them; they are even simpler. True, they cannot live by their own means, but Dauvillier's theory has come just in time to support their claims, and if it is correct, their claims have a good chance of being recognized. But if it came to a choice, we would put our money on the blue algae.

Conclusion

As we end this study, let us cast a last glance over our conclusions and draw up a balance sheet.

History has shown us how the problem was slowly defined, how, in the course of centuries, the number of species thought to arise from biogenesis was whittled down by careful observation. Pasteur decided the question once and for all with his supreme skill, and the belief that biogenesis was an impossibility became rooted in all educated minds.

We need only consider the differences between matter and life to justify this way of thought, and to show how easy and simple it is to make the distinction in theory. However, intermediate stages do exist—creatures so small and so simplified that it is possible to ask whether or not they are alive—and this doubt by itself shows that the distinction is still not at all clear in practice.

In order to explain the origin of life, materialists claim that nature can bridge the gap that separates it from life either by chance or by a dialectic process, while vitalists talk of creation.

No matter which of these positions we take, science tries to show us how things might have occurred, according to what we know of the world and its history. Life has not always existed on our globe and did not come from elsewhere, but suddenly appeared when the surrounding conditions made it possible. Dauvillier shows us, in his comprehensive theory, how ultraviolet light from the sun could have caused interesting syntheses of organic matter, from which, no doubt, life was born.

When we try to study this process with the help of paleontology, however, we find an almost complete lack of evidence for the first half of the period during which life has peopled the earth. There is no eyewitness who can dispel our doubts and tell us whether such and such a species of blue algae was really the first living thing. We are now and forever limited to speculations, with little chance of their one day becoming certitudes.

Index